C000171190

Locum Doctor
Survival Guide

about
locum123.com

Set up by a locum GP in 2001, locum123.com has become one of the UK's most popular locum websites.

locum123 is a fully automated locum messaging service, which allows locums to receive free SMS text message/email requests for locum cover from GP units and hospitals across the UK.

locum123 is NOT a locum agency – locum123 does not charge any commission on the work locums do. Use of the site is totally free, apart from asking health care units to pay for any SMS text messages they send.

Locums have total privacy (locum123 does not give out locum contact details to anyone) and total control over the service.

Locums can use their Locum Control Panel to:

- switch the service on/off
- choose between SMS and/or email notification
- select which areas in the UK to receive requests from
- choose which types of work they want
- update their online availability

locum123 is also developing a range of useful tools for locums – such as the income and tax calculator.

You can register online at http://www.locum123.com

locum123.com

Locum Doctor Survival Guide

Robbie Coull

First Edition
December 2005

Locum Doctor Survival Guide

by Robbie Coull

Copyright © 1999-2005 Robbie Coull.

Printed in the United Kingdom.

Published by locum123.com ltd, Suite 9, 24 Station Square, Inverness, Highland IV1 1LD.

Reproduction for personal or educational use

Permission granted to reproduce for personal and educational use without pecuniary or commercial interest or gain only. No changes may be made to the text or layout of copies made unless otherwise expressly stated (neither additions nor omissions). In all cases this copyright notice, and a link to the locum123.com website if present, must remain intact.

Commercial reproduction

All commercial rights are reserved.

No part of this book may be reproduced or transmitted in any form by any means electronic, mechanical, photocopying, recording, or otherwise, without the prior written permission of the author, except as detailed above under reproduction for personal or educational use.

For information on obtaining permission for commercial reprints or excerpts, contact publishing@locum123.com.

ISBN-13: 978-0-9552072-0-4

ISBN-10: 0-9552072-0-7

Disclaimer

Although every effort has been taken to check the factual details in this book, it is only intended as a guide. The locum world is a fast changing one, and some (or all) of the information will become out of date over time. Some of the information will even be out of date by the time this book is published.

> **Tip:**
>
> Updates and corrections of the advice in this book are posted on the locum123.com website, so visit the locum123 site to check for the most up to date information.

We hope that you find the contents of this guide useful, but it is provided 'as is' and without warranty. We cannot, of course, accept any liability for any errors or omissions, nor for the consequences of any action(s) taken/not taken based on this guide's contents.

For Ellie and Mirrie

TABLE OF CONTENTS

Foreword to online edition (2004)

I first started doing hospital locum work in 1994 after I finished my house jobs. I found that I really enjoyed travelling round and seeing how different parts of the country did things.

Over the next three years, I spent a year and a half doing locum hospital jobs while completing my own GP Vocational Training Scheme. After a year as a GP registrar in Stornoway, on the Isle of Lewis, I set up my own locum GP service in 1998.

Since then I have been doing locum GP work across the UK (and also for four months in Canada). It was a steep learning curve! When I started, I was being paid 'BMA rates' of £178 per 24 hours in small practices in the Highlands. I worked seven days a week, covering huge mileage, spending 42 weeks on the road, living out of a suitcase from B&B to B&B. I was shocked when my first tax bill showed that I had massive expenses from running round the country all the time, and I had actually only earned £30,000 for all that work. I could have earned two (or perhaps even three) times that if I had taken a nice partnership somewhere. There was no shortage of partnership vacancies, and I could have been at home with minimal on call for twice the money. My debts - left over from my student days - were not being paid off. Instead, I was borrowing more to make up for the shortfall in my income.

What particularly irked me was that I was turning down three times as much work as I was taking. Because of the locum shortage my mobile phone was ringing constantly with offers of work. Also, the principals seemed to think that locums were really expensive, and that I earned far more than them!

If the OFT had not stepped in 1999 and forbidden the BMA to set locum rates, that would probably have been the end of my career as a locum. But I embarked on a programme of gradually raising my locum rates until in 2003 I could finally earn an average GP income and only be away from home for around half of the year.

In the mean time, in 2001, I was setting up the locum123.com website to make it easier for surgeries in the Highlands to contact locums re: work (and to stop my mobile from ringing all the time!). This proved extremely popular, and is now used by locums, GP surgeries, and hospitals all over the UK.

However, as locum rates went up, criticism from principals increased – rumours abounded in Highland that some locums earned three times as much as the GPs there, when in reality locum earnings were rarely above the average income level for a GP in Scotland. A couple of GPs even made these claims in public meetings and conferences that I attended, and accused 'high earning' locums of worsening the recruitment crisis. It was obvious that many GPs had a hopelessly simplistic view of what locum work really involved. They needed more accurate information about the financial and practical realities of locum work. So I produced the Locum Income and Tax Calculator (initially for coull.net but the updated version is now on locum123.com).

As more GPs either decided to avoid partnerships and stay locum doctors, or to leave partnerships to become locums, it became increasingly clear that there was a shortage of locum advice and information for them. This shortage of information meant that new locums were having to learn the hard way. Some of us tried, with limited success, to introduce some teaching material on locum work for GP registrars, but we met resistance from the GPs running the VTS schemes. It seems that many VTS organisers still do not believe in teaching doctors to become locums. I don't know whether this is a form of snobbery, or whether it is a cynical attempt to maintain a pool of 'uneducated' locums who are more easily exploited by practices. Even the old 'NANP Yellow Book' has not been updated since 1997 and contains such un-PC comments as 'Am I welcome to have a coffee with the principals?'

It seemed that a comprehensive guide to modern GP locum work was long overdue.

I had already produced some practical advice pages for locums on my coull.net website, and I had transferred some of these over to the locum123.com website. Meanwhile, although the NANP[*] website discussion forum was pretty quiet, there was a growing and vibrant non-principal discussion forum on DNUK[**]. So, my thanks to everyone on the DNUK NP discussion forum for the ideas, advice, tips, suggestions, criticisms and encouragement that have (almost) all gone into this guide.

Robbie Coull

locum@coull.net

Inverness, July 2004

---

[*] National Association of Non-Principals, now the National Association of Sessional GPs (NASGP) http://www.nasgp.org.uk - the discussion forum has since been removed

[**] Doctors.net.uk (DNUK) – http://www.doctors.net.uk - a very active NP forum. Many of the locums on the DNUK NP discussion forum have their own websites, which are listed in Appendix A

Foreword to paperback edition (2005)

Well, it's been over a year since the online edition of the Locum Doctor Survival Guide first appeared on locum123.com. In that time, the guide has proved very popular. It has continued to be updated and expanded with further suggestions and ideas, many of them coming from questions asked by locums on the doctors.net.uk[*] non-principal forum and from the locum123.com comments form.

The guide has now grown to over three times the size of the first online edition. This increase in size means that what started off as a reasonably chunky guide has now become a proper book, and that printing it out, or reading it as a pdf file on a computer, has become more and more of a hassle. So, by the wonders of Publish on Demand technology, I've toiled away in the small hours to produce this paperback edition, which should be kinder to the eye and printer cartridge.

During this process, as I was surfing the net one night, I came across a locum in a discussion forum who said something along the

---

[*] Doctors.net.uk (DNUK) – http://www.doctors.net.uk - still a very active NP forum, Many of the locums on the DNUK NP discussion forum have their own websites, which are listed in Appendix A

lines of "The Locum Doctor Survival Guide is essential reading, but it's also a great cure for insomnia". So, in the interests of keeping readers awake, I've spiced the book up a bit by adding notes, tips, anecdotes, warnings, and examples.

> ***Tips, Anecdotes, Examples, and Warnings:***
>
> Are highlighted inside boxes like this one.

Please do continue to let me know what you like and don't like about the book, if there are any topics that you would like to see added, or if you just have a question about locum work that is not answered by this book. In the likely event that I don't know the answer myself, I should at least be able to point you in the direction of someone that does.

I hope that you find this book useful, and that you have a happy and successful time as a locum.

Robbie Coull

locum@coull.net

Inverness, September 2005

Chapter 1:
Introduction to Locum Work

Who is this book for?

The Locum Doctor Survival Guide is primarily intended for GP locums in the UK, but should contain information that is of use to all locum doctors.

This book is aimed at:

- GP registrars who are looking at locum work – either as a career, or as a temporary option - after they finish their VTS training.

- GP principals who are thinking of 'jumping ship' and are worried about the financial and practical aspects of the freelance life.

- GPs who are already locums, and who will hopefully discover useful gems here as well (if you know of any gems that are missing, then please do let me know so that I can add them!).

As many sections as possible have been written with hospital locums in mind too. The reasons for this are three fold.

1. There are lots of areas of overlap between hospital and GP locum work.

2. Many GPs do some hospital locums as well (eg: Accident and Emergency and Psychiatry).

3. There is no authoritative book for hospital locums, so I figured that a few useful sections in a book for GPs was better than nothing.

Note:

If there are any hospital locums out there with a talent for writing who would like to write some chapters about hospital locum work for the next edition of this book, then let me know.

For conciseness, I have tried to stick to topics that pose unique problems for locums (such as the setting of locum rates), or to issues where locum work will necessitate a slightly different approach (such as arranging a mortgage, or the use of chaperones).

Advantages of Locum Work

Locum work is varied, interesting and exciting. Many doctors choose locum work over a formal NHS career because of the flexibility that locum work offers, and because locums can avoid much of the bureaucracy and over-management that makes working in the NHS such a trial. Others like the travel, and the fact that you can work in so many different environments.

However, locum work is also difficult, and can be lonely. You need to be self-sufficient, have an open mind and be able to make friends quickly and easily. It helps if you are flexible, able to improvise, and able to cope with wide variations in normal practice, style and delivery.

You will be called on to treat patients that you have never seen before (and may never see again) with the help of staff you don't know in an environment that is unfamiliar.

Starting locum work can still be a daunting prospect as there is seldom someone to show you how it is done (since it is unusual to have more than one locum in the unit or practice at any one time) and many of its elements are not taught in medical school - advertising, agreeing/haggling rates, billing etc..

This book is designed to answer all your questions and make locum work easier, less stressful and more rewarding.

For questions about the use of the locum123.com website, see our online help pages[*].

Types of Locum Work

There is a huge variety of locum work, and there are several ways to classify the different kinds of locum work.

Locum work can be hospital or primary care work, and can be arranged directly or via a locum agency. Also, locums may want to work full or part time, and may be willing to travel to residential locums.

There are also the less common types of locum work - such as in remote areas, foreign lands, prisons, cruise ships, and the armed services.

---

[*] http://www.locum123.com/help.shtml

One example is:

	Agency Work	**Self arranged work**
Hospital medicine	Hospital Agency Locum	Self arranged Hospital Locum
General Practice	GP Agency Locum	Self arranged GP locum

Another way to classify locum work is:

	Full Time	**Part Time**
Willing to travel	Full time residential locum work	Occasional or part time residential locum work ("Busman's holiday")
Working from home	Full time non-residential locum work in practices within a specified area.	Part time non-residential locum work in practices within a specified area.

It is this variety that makes locum work so appealing – you can find a style and type of locum work that suits your lifestyle.

So, now that you are sold on the idea of being a locum, the next thing is to work out how to go about finding work as a locum.

Chapter 2:
How to Find Locum Work

Planning ahead

Most locums tend to book locum work around two to three months in advance. Any longer than this, and you risk having bookings for times of the year that you have not had a chance to plan for yet, and less than this and you can start to get worried about paying that mortgage and putting food on the table.

However, it's important to remember when you are starting out in locum work, that although it is possible to get locum work at short notice (especially if you are willing to travel), it is best to plan ahead and start to book locum work at least a couple of months in advance.

GP locums should beware booking locum work if they are uncertain of when their Vocational Training certificate of satisfactory completion will arrive. If in doubt, you may want to take a few weeks holiday at the end of your VTS while you get organised[*].

---

[*] see Chapter 11:Important note for GP Registrars coming to the end of their training.

Finding locum work via locum123.com

Register your details and work preferences on the locum123.com web site[*] and you can receive notification of locum work that matches your settings via SMS text message and/or email.

You can select what kinds of locum work you would like to hear about, which postcodes/parts of the country you are keen to work in, which dates you are available and how you would like to be notified.

Because locum123 is fully automated, you can switch it on or off at any time, and you can update your settings instantly. This makes locum123.com the easiest and most hassle-free way to manage your locum requests.

Finding locum work via a locum agency

Obviously, at locum123.com we can't imagine why you would want to sign up with a locum agency when you have us, but a book about locum work would not be complete without a section on how to get the best out of locum agencies should you choose to use them.

Agencies are the most common route for locum hospital work, but are a much less common route for GPs.

What basically happens is that:

- You register with an agency and send them your CV, GMC and other documentation

- The agencies are contacted by hospitals/practices when they need locum cover.

---

[*] http://www.locum123.com

- Each agency phones round the list of doctors on their books until they find someone who is available and willing to work.

- Each agency then puts that doctor forward to the hospital/practice by faxing a CV through to them.

- Whichever agency provides an acceptable locum first gets the placement.

- The successful agency contacts the doctor they put forward and gives them reporting details.

- You turn up and do the work (if you are asked to work beyond your agreed hours make a note of them)

- You fill in the time sheet and fax/post it to the agency

- The agency pays you directly by PAYE. This means they will take off your tax and NI contributions before they pay you. (You are not self employed if you work exclusively for agencies - you will not qualify for the NHS pension scheme and will not be able to deduct as many expenses from your tax bill[*]). You should be paid within one to two weeks at the most.

> ### *Note:*
>
> The agency makes a profit by charging the hospital more than your hourly rate and keeping the difference (agency commission), so remember that they work for you and not the other way round (although really it's a symbiotic relationship!). Agency commission rates vary, but are usually around 20% to 50% on top of the fee you receive.

---

[*] See Chapter 6: Tax and National Insurance

Now there are a few problems here, which are important to bear in mind.

- You need to be instantly and easily contactable if you are going to get work, or the agency will find someone else as it's usually first come first served.

Tip:

Avoid giving agencies your home phone number as they will ring you at the most inconvenient times to check your availability etc. (and may continue to do this for years after you have stopped working for them!).

- The hospitals usually fill locums internally, so most of the time you will agree to go forward for work but not get it. This is normal - don't let it demoralize you.

- If you work for several agencies you need to keep careful note of who is offering you what work. You may go forward for two posts at the same time and if you are accepted for both you will need to turn one down, which can make you unpopular with the agency involved.

- Some agencies will put several doctors forward for the same locum to increase their chances of success. This will reduce your success rate and mean you will spend a lot of time answering the phone! Avoid such agencies if at all possible.

- GPs should note that agency work cannot be entered into the NHS pension scheme[*].

To work out which agencies to join, ask around the area(s) you want to work to see what agencies are popular there. Contact personnel departments at the local hospitals and ask which agencies they use, or look out for locums working at the hospitals (the canteens at lunchtime are a good place to start) and ask them which agencies they use.

---

[*] See Chapter 9: Pensions

Remember that agencies are not all the same. Rates vary, as do their abilities to place you effectively, and some agencies will be much more pushy (or may even be misleading) in order to fill a placement and get the commission. So choose carefully. If you are unhappy with an agency, change to a different one.

It is common to be listed with 2 or 3 agencies at a time to improve your choice of work, but any more than this and your phone will never stop ringing.

Organising locums yourself

You can of course go about organising locums yourself without the help of locum123.com or locum agencies.

For hospital locums you should contact the personnel departments of the hospitals you are interested in working in and ask them to add you to their list of locum doctors. They will then contact you if they need locum cover.

In general practice you can send your details to practices in the areas that you are keen to work. You can obtain details of the practices in your area in the Yellow Pages or via your LMC/PCT. A short tabulated page (single side of A4) with your contact details, availability, and synopsis of your CV is the best format.

Many areas have local locum groups that distribute lists of locums to the practices in their areas. They usually have an annual fee for this (usually around £10-20 per year) but can be an invaluable source of local knowledge, post-graduate education and just general camaraderie. Some still have a locally agreed rates structure, but this is viewed as being a breach of the Competition Act 1998, so this should now be rare. You can contact them via the NASGP website[*].

Most PCOs make the list of locum GPs in their area accessible to practices in their area.

Ask practice managers or other locums in your chosen areas how they find locums, or contact the local Dean of Postgraduate General Practice (usually attached to the local Medical School) for advice.

---

[*] http://www.nasgp.org.uk.

Chapter 3:
Running Your Own Business

Introduction to running your own business

In this chapter we are going to look at how to set up and manage your locum business – either as a self-employed locum, or a director in your own limited company, or a partner in a partnership. Locums who are employees (for example hospital locums, or GP locums employed by a PCO or locum agency) don't have any of these hassles, but should still find some bits of this chapter useful.

Principals who are switching to locum work may already have experience of running a business, but most locums will not have any experience or training in this (other than the instruction in practice finance/management that they receive as a registrar).

Most locums run a single-person business (or may employ their spouse in some capacity) - few have access to a manager or other clerical staff – but the principles are the same for both large and small businesses.

Turnover, Profits and Salaries

An employee has a salary, which is usually pretty fixed each month (expenses payments aside). Their employer deducts tax and pension contributions etc. at source, so it is pretty clear to employees how much money they are actually earning.

However, business finances consist of:

- **Turnover** - the money that you are paid for work done.

- **Expenses** – the money that you spend in the pursuance of your business.

- **Gross profit** – the business profit which you have left after your expenses.

- **Tax-free deductions** – pension contributions and other personal deductions that are tax free.

- **Tax** – the tax you pay on your profit.

- **Taxed deductions** – pension and other personal deductions that are not tax free.

- **Net profit** – the money you have left to spend after your expenses, tax, pension, and national insurance.

It's a common error for a new locum to mistake their turnover (the money practices pay them for the work) with their previous salary as an employee. This can make it appear that you are earning far more than you really are.

Setting up your business

Setting up shop as a self-employed locum GP is pretty straightforward. All you need to do is:

- Decide if you want a name for your business - most locums simply use their own name, but you can 'trade as' another name – eg: Dr Joe Bloggs trading as (t/a) Bloggs Locum Cover.

- Decide if you want to have a separate business bank account (see section below).

- Notify your local HM Revenue and Customs office that you are going to become self-employed – they will send you a form to fill in and a direct debit mandate so you can pay your National Insurance contributions.

Caution:

You must inform HM Revenue and Customs[*] of your change to self-employment status within three months, otherwise you may face a £100 fine.

Setting up as a partnership or limited company is a bit more complicated, and is described in more detail below.

Self Employment, Partnerships and Limited Companies

Self Employment

This is the tax status of most locum GPs. Self employed means that you work for yourself as a one-person business.

Self employed GPs contract their services to practices, PCTs and Health Boards and issue invoices for the work done. At the end of each tax year, you complete a tax return and pay tax based on your profit. Your profit is your turnover (how much money you were paid for locum work) minus

---

[*] HM Revenue and Customs is the new department that merged the old Inland Revenue and HM Customs and Excise departments.

any allowable expenses. Your actual take home income is this profit minus any tax and deductions (pension, national insurance etc.).

Note that it is the tax man who has the final say over whether you are self employed or not. Amongst other things, the tax man will be looking at the following:

	Self Employed	**Employee**
Invoice	Issues own invoices	Is given a pay slip
Rates of pay	Sets own charges	Is offered a rate of pay
Work pattern	Chooses when to work	Is told when to work
Holiday pay	No	Yes
Sick pay	No	Yes
Paid study leave	No	Yes
Number of customers	Multiple customers	Single employer

Note that you can be employed for some work (eg: salaried post) and self-employed for other work (eg: OOH locum sessions) at the same time.

The advantage of being self-employed is that there are more things that you can claim as allowable expenses. This means that a proportion of the cost of many items that you use (such as your car, computer etc.) are tax free. This can mean tax savings of up to 40% on the cost of these items.

However, there is far more paperwork involved, you will probably need the assistance of an accountant, and it is not possible to spread your tax liability with your spouse (other than paying him/her a small salary for secretarial work etc.).

Partnerships

A partnership is a group of people who jointly own a business. Most GPs in the UK work in partnerships, but very few locums work in partnerships.

Husband and wife partnerships

From a tax point of view, partnerships are similar to being self-employed. The advantage for locums is that they can set up a partnership with their spouse and split the profits in the company – thereby spreading the tax liability between the two of you.

This can be useful if the spouse earns below the 40% tax bracket threshold, as they will pay less tax than you on some of the money they receive from the partnership.

Locum chambers

A recent development is the formation of 'virtual practices' or locum chambers by groups of locum GPs. This allows locums to get together in an area set a common locum rate[*] and share the costs of employing a manager or secretary to do their paperwork and bookings for them. It also allows the GPs to have a formal support network for education etc..

Partnerships should have a formal, partnership agreement between the partners which can be used to settle disputes. You should contact a solicitor with experience of partnership law for advice on this.

Limited Liability Partnerships

As the name suggests, this is a partnership with some of the limited liability that you would normally associate with a limited company. This is

---

[*] Because a partnership is considered as a single 'undertaking' under the Competition Act 1998, this is legal (whereas if several locums who were not in a partnership agreed on locum rates, they would be operating an illegal cartel – see the Chapter 4: Setting Locum Rates).

a relatively new form of business, but could be useful for many small businesses that otherwise would have the hassle and expense of setting up a limited company.

Limited Companies

Public Companies limited by guarantee (using the suffix Ltd.) became more popular recently due to tax breaks for small businesses. However, these tax breaks have been reversed in the 2004 budget, making limited companies less attractive.

A limited company is a legal entity in its own right. It can employ staff and own property. The company itself is owned by shareholders while being run by a group of at least two company directors (who can also be shareholders). The liability of the owners (shareholders) for the company extends only to the value of their shares. So, should the business become bankrupt, the owner's personal assets are not threatened (except for any outstanding tax liability, which the company directors are personally responsible for). Limited companies require more paperwork and have higher accounting costs.

Normally, for a GP and spouse who want to set up a limited company, they each receive a nominal 50 shares in the company. Then the company pays them each a salary, and they receive the balance of their income as dividends on the shares. Dividends are the division of the company profits equally to each shareholder (ie: if there are 100 shares, then you get 1% of the profit for each share that you hold).

Taxation is more complex. The company pays corporation tax on its profits (around 20%). You pay tax normally on your salary (this is an expense for the company, so it does not pay corporation tax in this). If your income enters the 40% tax bracket, you then pay tax on any dividend income that is above the 40% threshold[*].

The other advantage of limited companies is that you can limit your liability. If the company becomes bankrupt, your personal assets are largely protected (apart from unpaid company tax).

---

[*] See Chapter 6: Tax and National Insurance.

Limited Company Summary:

Not worth the hassle for the vast majority of locum GPs.

Advantages:

- You may be able to spread the tax burden with a low-earning/non-earning spouse (but a partnership is easier and achieves the same ends)

- You can give out shares in the company, should you wish to give money to your kids (university etc.) at a tax advantage (but see comments about tax evasion below).

- You can keep money in the company from a heavy year, and take it out later during a low income year to minimise tax liability (eg: saving for retirement)

- You have limited liability should things go wrong (not an issue for locum GPs, but nice for other things such as if you have property you rent out etc., but you can also form a Limited Liability Partnership with less hassle.)

- The company can own items separately (eg: property)

- PCTs are sometimes more willing to deal with a company than a self employed locum.

- It may give you a stronger position in disputes with a PCT/practice (as you are an employee of another company).

Disadvantages:

- Significantly more paperwork

- More complex legal position.

- Extra insurance costs.

- Higher accountancy costs.

- Dividend payments for what is essentially 'hourly' work (ie: locum cover) are controversial. Dividends were designed to be a way of distributing extra profit, not as an alternative to employee salaries. It's strictly speaking legal to avoid tax this way (cf. evasion which is illegal) but the tax man does not like it.

Caution:

Minimum wage legislation applies even to employee-owners. For example, if you work 150 hours per month for your company, but only pay yourself £300 per month, then you will be committing a criminal offence by paying yourself below the minimum wage.

• You can't NHS superannuate the earnings, as you are a company employee.

• Any salary that you pay (to yourself or any other employee) that is above the employee's tax-free threshold (around £4000 per year) attracts an employers National Insurance contribution of around 11%.

The easiest way to set up a limited company is usually through a solicitor. An empty company can be purchased for around £300. You can specify any currently unused name for your company, and should receive a certificate of incorporation and a company pack with all the paperwork, share certificates, sample minutes for your first board meeting, and a company seal to use on official documents. Make sure you use a reputable company to set this up for you – you don't want to find out later that the company you have bought still has outstanding liabilities.

Caution:

At the time of going to press, taxation of 'husband and wife' dividends is the subject of a test court case (which has gone to appeal). You should discuss your dividend tax situation with an experienced accountant.

Business banking

Business cheque accounts

You should really consider opening a separate business cheque account, although many locums simply use their own personal current account.

Advantages of business accounts	Disadvantages of business accounts
Banks can object to the use of a personal account for the purpose of running a small business.	Unless you are depositing large numbers of cheques in your personal bank account, the banks are unlikely to raise any concerns.
Having a business account keeps your business and personal finances separate, and makes accounting easier.	Having a business account involves extra paperwork.
Business accounts are supposed to offer either interest on the money in the account, or free banking.	Personal accounts usually offer both free banking and interest payments, so business banking usually works out more expensive.
	You usually don't have access to a cheque guarantee card in a business account.

If you are going to set up a partnership or limited company, then a separate business account is mandatory.

Cheque Guarantee Cards

Business accounts do not usually issue cheque guarantee cards, so you will find that cheques are not accepted in many retail situations.

> **Sartorial note:**
>
> You usually get to choose whether to be issued with standard sized cheques (the same size as personal cheques) or the larger 'business' sized cheques.

Business Credit Cards

It is useful to have a business credit card for business purchases and expenses, especially if you intend to pay for goods over the phone or the internet. Also, since most business accounts do not have a cheque guarantee card, you will need to use a credit card to purchase many items from shops and retailers.

Tip:

Credit cards (eg: Visa™ and Mastercard™) offer better protection in the case of internet or telephone fraud than debit cards.

There is a system called 'chargeback' for any payments that are made to a company by credit card without the cardholder being physically present (ie: over the telephone or by internet). These are called 'Cardholder Not Present' transactions, and the cardholder can challenge the payment up to six months after it is made.

Should you find that an unauthorised transaction has taken place, or that you did not receive the goods or services that you paid for, then you can request a 'chargeback' from your card provider.

In the case of chargebacks, it is the responsibility of the seller to prove that you were supplied with goods or services.

These protections do not exist using debit cards (such as Switch/Maestro).

In the case of a limited company or limited liability partnership, obtaining a business credit card can be difficult and expensive, and usually involves agreeing to personally guarantee the debt. It is often simpler, and cheaper, in these circumstances to obtain a personal credit card which is used purely for business purposes.

In either case, it makes accounting simpler if you have separate credit cards for business and personal use.

Tip:

You can simplify keeping track of your business expenses by using different credit cards for different types of purchase.

For example, you could use one credit card solely for vehicle expenses (petrol, insurance, repairs etc.), and keep another credit card purely for office expenses (computers, printers, printer cartridges, paper, envelopes etc.).

This means that your expense categories are quite clear at the end of the year.

You should, of course, pay each card off in full at the end of each month from your main current account, if at all possible, in order to avoid interest payments.

Business loans and overdrafts

You should have a named business manager assigned to you when you open a business account. You can discuss any borrowing needs with him/her, but bear in mind that they are not independent and may not give you the best advice.

It is often simpler and cheaper to obtain personal borrowing via a low interest personal loan or low interest credit card (for short term borrowing – the interest rates usually rise steeply after a short period).

You can release equity in your home or other property at a low interest rate, but beware the effect of paying off such borrowing over a longer period of time (which can make this a very expensive form of borrowing), or any penalties for repaying the amount early.

Employing other people

Reasons to become an employer

Being an employer instead of an employee is a key aspect of running your own business. Although locum GPs are usually sole traders, there are significant advantages to employing someone to help you.

For example, you may want to employ a part time secretary or even a part time practice manager. Some locums are beginning to get together to set up 'virtual practices' in which they employ a practice manager to run the business side of their locum business*.

More commonly, locums will want to employ their spouse so that they can pay them for the work that they do (for example, taking bookings over the phone, or secretarial work).

> *Anecdote:*
>
> When I was contracted by a health board to run a vacant single handed practice for nine months, I was able to employ my wife (a nurse) to carry out some of the treatment room nursing duties that had been performed by the previous GP's nurse wife.

Employer's tax responsibilities

Employers normally have to run a payroll for their staff, and this includes collecting PAYE tax for HM Revenue and Customs and paying the employers' National Insurance contribution (which is around 12% on top of their salary).

---

* See previous section on Locum Chambers for more details.

Thankfully, these responsibilities do not apply for part-time employees who earn below a certain threshold. This is around £3,000 to £4,000 per year.

You should check with your accountant to make sure that you are complying with applicable regulations.

Employing your spouse

You can employ your spouse to perform some of the duties of the business. You can then claim his or her salary as an expense.

This can be useful if your spouse is a lower band tax payer (ie: they are not earning enough to pay any tax at the higher rate), but you are. Your spouse will then not pay as much tax on this salary as you would if you took it as profit, so you can maximise your joint tax allowances.

Caution:

So long as the amount you pay your spouse is justified (in the form of work that they carry out) then this is perfectly legal. However, if you pay your spouse a salary for work that is not done simply to reduce your tax burden, then this is considered to be tax evasion, which is illegal[*].

Employer's legal responsibilities

As an employer, you will need to comply with employment law as regards public liability insurance for employees, paid holiday leave, sick leave, and so on.

It's also important to understand the rights of employees when it comes to pay, conditions, and termination of employment. For example, you must

---

[*] see Chapter 6: Tax and National Insurance

pay employees (even yourself in the case of a limited company) the legal minimum hourly wage. Failure to do so can result in criminal prosecution.

Such legal advice is outside the scope of this book, but there are books on employment law available in most good bookshops, and you should take advice from a suitable solicitor.

Data Protection Act (1998)

When you start up as a locum GP, you will be storing data about your customers (GP surgeries, PCTs, Acute Trusts etc.) and about your patients.

You are required by law to register with the Information Commissioner[*] when maintaining such records. The 2004 registration fee was £35 per year[†].

---

[*] The Office of the Information Commissioner has replaced the Data Protection Registrar.

[†] See Appendix B: Useful addresses

website: http://www.informationcommissioner.gov.uk

Caution:

You should consider what security arrangements you have to protect confidential data that you store. Locking filing cabinets and password protection of your computer, for example.

This depends on your personal circumstances, but it's best not to find your seven year old has taking Mrs Smith's hysterectomy report in to 'Show and Tell', or that your flatmate has borrowed your laptop to surf the net, and is now horrified to find out what really goes on at the local GUM clinic.

Chapter 4:
Setting Locum Rates

Introduction

How to go about setting a locum rate is the topic that generates the most discussion from GPs new to the locum scene. This is as it should be, as charging the wrong rate for their work is the most costly mistake that most locums will ever make.

However, the first thing to point out is that there is no simple answer to the universally asked question 'what should I charge as a GP locum?' The simple reason for this is that the Office of Fair Trading has ruled that anyone setting rates for self-employed GP locums is breaking the Competition Act 1998 (more of that later in the chapter).

So the complicated, but correct, answer to the question is 'you can charge whatever you want'. By the end of this chapter, you should have a much better idea of what you want to charge.

Different types of locum rates

Sessions

GPs in the UK tend to work in units of time referred to as 'sessions'. A session has various definitions, but basically there are two sessions per day and most full time GP work between seven and eight clinical sessions per week. Because of this, many locums charge practices by the session (and therefore have a sessional rate).

Sessional rates can cause confusion when it comes to how much work is actually included per session, so many GPs qualify this by specifying how many hours are in a session (usually 3-4hrs)

Short sessions

Practices are increasingly looking for shorter sessions than the traditional 3-4hr session. Many practices ask locums to provide a 2 hour session.

This can be a problem for locums, as it is rarely possible to fill the missing hours with work. It is wise to consider charging the first hour of any session at a higher rate (say 150% of the normal rate), to compensate for this.

Also, make sure that the practice realises that sessions include a time for 'tidying up' paperwork at the end (many locums allow 30 minutes at the end of each session for this). A two hour session is often a 2.5 hour session in reality, which will need to be factored into your rate.

Hourly rates

Some locums ignore sessions altogether and charge an hourly rate. Hourly rates are useful for other types of work, such as on-call and private work, and most locums vary their rate for unsocial hours etc..

Supplementary charges for visits

Many locums charge an extra fee for home visits (for example £x per visit on top of, or instead of, the normal rate).

The disadvantage of this form of invoicing is that it is difficult to know the exact cost of locum cover in advance, which can make budgeting difficult for both the practice and the locum.

Other locums include a set time per visit (eg: 30 minutes), but this can cause problems if you are unable to find the house easily or the practice is rural.

Charging for on call (or Duty Doctor) work

Practices often ask locums to provide Duty Doctor cover during the day (for example from 8am to 6pm). This is usually tied to one or two normal sessions, but can be just stand-alone on call work. Often the doctor can be on call from home, or whilst having lunch.

Charging for this type of cover is more complex, because the workload varies enormously from practice to practice, and from day to day, but there are several common strategies:

Flat hourly rate

Many locums feel that on call time is time working and charge their normal hourly rate for time on call. The advantages of this are that the fee is clear in advance and there is no possibility of the locum being taken advantage of with a heavy on call. The disadvantage is that it is often prohibitively expensive for the practice.

Day rate

Some locums charge a day rate which includes on call cover plus a certain amount of actual clinical work. They then charge extra if the workload is greater than the included amount. The advantages of the Day Rate are that quiet well-organised practices are rewarded with affordable on call cover, and the locum is protected against poorly organised or busy practices by being able to charge extra if the workload is high. The disadvantage is that the final fee is not set and practices can get a nasty shock if the workload is significantly greater than they anticipated.

On call rate

Other locums have a different rate for on call work (especially on call from home). For example, they may charge 50% of their standard rate for on call work. The advantages of a set on call rate are that it is affordable for practices and the fee is clear in advance. The disadvantage is that the fee is not linked to the intensity of work, which can lead to the locum being taken advantage of.

Call out fee

Some locums do not charge for the on call hours, but charge a call out fee (or an hourly rate plus a call out fee) for any calls received when on call. This type of fee was more common when the old BMA rates were in effect pre-1999, but is much less common now. The advantage is that the on call is cheap for the practice, but the disadvantages are that there is huge variation in the fee and the locum may end up being on call for free.

On call rate with call out fee

A few locums combine the above on call rate with a call out fee. Again, this was more common pre-1999 with the old BMA rates.

Example:

Day Rate in practice

The Anytown Practice asks Lorna Locum to cover their practice from 8am until 6pm from her home (Lorna lives nearby), and to do two sessions each involving a three hour surgery and some paperwork.

Lorna agrees to a day rate of £500, but specifies in her terms and conditions that this day rate only includes up to 7 hours of clinical work during the 10 hours. If the workload is greater, there will be a £70 per hour surcharge pro rata.

Lorna provides two 3.5 hours sessions of consultations and some paperwork. She then goes home but receives an emergency call at 5.30pm which takes 30 minutes to deal with.

As the total workload was 7.5 hours, Lorna invoices the practice £500 for the day rate plus £35 for the extra half hour (£535 in total).

Methods for deciding what rates to charge

Hospital locum rates are often set, either by the agency or by the hospital, although they may be open to negotiation, especially in hard-pressed specialities.

If you are organizing your own General Practice locums then you need to agree a rate with the practice before you begin work. This is the part that everyone, including the most hardened haggler, finds most difficult.

There are essentially three ways to decide on rates:

1. Local rates

Find out what others in your area are charging, and charge the same. This is the most common and least difficult method for setting rates. However, it is also produces the lowest profits for locum doctors.

> *Caution*:
>
> Although it is perfectly legal for locums to tell each other how much they charge, it is illegal for one or more locums (or employers) to get together and set common locum rates/terms (see Office of Fair Trading and Cartels).

2. Market forces

This involves charging 'what the market will bear', and involves applying the principal of supply and demand. This method is most effective when there is a shortage of locums and a high demand for locum cover (which is the current market situation in most parts of the UK). In such circumstances, this method is the best way to maximise your profits.

To use this method, choose a starting rate (possible based on local rates, as above), then increase your rate periodically by a small percentage (eg: 10% increase every couple of months). You may want to vary your rates based on high/low demand times of the year (eg: school holidays).

As your rate increases, you will notice that there is less demand for your services, but you will be earning more money for the work you are doing. The trick is to find the correct balance where demand is just high enough to produce the desired level of income with the minimum amount of effort.

The danger with this method is that you end up pricing yourself out of the market altogether, and will then need to reduce your rate again to find enough work (which can be quite humbling!). Also, this method is very sensitive to even small changes in the locum market – if a few more locums start working in your area, or demand for locum cover falls, then you may find yourself suddenly without work until you lower your rates.

Example:

Dr Lorna Locum is charging £30 per hour for 30 hours of locum cover per week. So she is earning £900 per week for this work.

But Lorna is being offered over 100 hours of work per week, and so is having to turn down lots of work because she can only work 30 hours per week due to family commitments.

Lorna increases her locum rate to £60 per hour.

Demand falls because practices decide to use other, cheaper, locums so she is now only able to book 20 hours of locum work per week.

But even with only 20 hours of work Lorna now earns £1200 per week, a third more than she was earning before.

Also, since she is working less hours, Lorna's annual expenses have fallen by a third as well.

So overall Lorna's profits have increased by over 33% while her workload has fallen by 33%. So Lorna has a better income AND more time to spend with her children.

3. Income calculation

This method involves taking the amount of money that you think you should earn each year ('target income'), adding your estimated annual expenses, and then dividing the total by the number of sessions that you plan to work. You can then use this figure as your target rate per session.

You can use two locum123 resources to help you calculate your rates using this method:

Locum Income Spreadsheet

You can download this spreadsheet in excel format from the locum123 website[*], and you can use it to calculate your hourly rate based on your expenses, preferred workload, and target income.

Locum Income and Tax Calculator

You can use the locum123 online income and tax calculator[†] to estimate your income, expenses, and tax liability based on figures that you feed into it. Very useful for trying out different combinations of workloads and rates.

Out of Hours work

Out of Hours (OOH) rates are more difficult, because many locums vary the OOH rate depending on the rota and the size of the population covered (see the section on Working Out of Hours). However, the same methods as above can be applied to OOH rates as well.

Locum auctions

In the future, locums auctioning available sessions to practices may become popular as a method to maximise locum profits without having to negotiate or haggle rates. The Department of Health is rumoured to be interested in 'auctioning locum work to the lowest bidder', but with the current locum doctor shortage this is unlikely to be effective (you need to have more than one interested bidder for an auction to work). However, markets change and should we end up with a glut of locums in the future, then an auction system is a possibility.

---

[*] http://www.locum123.com/survival_pack.shtml

[†] http://www.locum123.com/calculator.cgi

Other factors to take into account when setting your rates

Time as a locum

How much of your career do you plan to spend being a locum? This will impact how much of an investment you want to make in being a locum, such as taking out income protection, a private pension, buying office and computer equipment, building up your own supply of medical equipment or organizing mail forwarding.

Travelling and residential locum work

How far from home are you willing to go to get work? This, of course, depends on personal circumstances and preference. However, if you want to be able to choose when you work and want to be paid decent rates, but still want to work full time, then you will almost certainly have to be willing to travel away from home at least part of the time.

The two key elements of residential locum work are communication and accommodation. Communication determines how long you can be a locum before your life falls apart. Accommodation on the other hand determines how long you can be a locum before you fall apart.

Accommodation can vary from a mattress on the floor of a nurses dormitory to a four star hotel. Imagine how you would feel after four weeks without a break on a camp bed with no electricity, only a coal fire to keep you warm, an outside toilet and shower and a broken down stove to cook on - then imagine how you would feel if it had been four weeks in a warm hotel with a good bed, TV, an en suite shower and bath and good food. I've done both (although I only managed one week on the camp bed!).

If you do a lot of residential work, and you want to maintain a semblance of a normal life, then even with excellent communication and accommodation you will still need to take more time off than if you were working from home. You will need this time to travel to and from locums, rest, restock / re-supply and spend time with family and friends – for example, two weeks on and one week off or one week on and one week off. You're rates should reflect this.

Remember, if you do travel away from home, you will have more choice in where you work, so you should expect to negotiate better rates and good accommodation.

Workload

How much work do you want to do each week/month/year? This will affect the income you can earn based on the rates that you are able to charge. Bear in mind that some expenses are fixed, and so the less work you do, the greater the expense to profit ratio.

You can use the Locum Income and Tax Calculator[*] or Locum Income Spreadsheet[†] to see how different levels of workload will affect your expenses and profits.

Income requirements

You need to know how much you have to earn each month as a minimum to stay solvent Sit down and work out your monthly outgoing expenses: mortgage/rent, utility bills, mobile phone costs, vehicle costs, MDU indemnity and other medical subscriptions.

Once you've worked out how much will go out each month add on how much you think you will spend per week on routine things like food, petrol, entertainment etc.. Add all this up and subtract any other income you receive to work out how much you need to earn each month.

It is wise to have access to three times this amount in savings or credit in case you should hit a slow period or fall ill for a couple of months.

---

[*] http://www.locum123.com/calculator.cgi

[†] http://www.locum123.com/survival_pack.shtml

Peak times for locum requests

locum123 receives thousands of locum requests each year. The number of locum requests posted by practices varies with the time of year, as shown in this table:

Month (2003)	Percentage of requests sent
January	8.6%
February	9.8%
March	11.0%
April	10.5%
May	10.4%
June	10.2%
July	7.6%
August	6.6%
September	6.9%
October	6.4%
November	7.2%
December	4.8%

Note: these figures reflect the months that practices sent their request, not the months that they were booking cover for (most practices request cover 2-8 weeks in advance).

This shows that spring and early summer are the most popular times for practices to organise locum cover (as they prepare for the summer holidays).

Covering absent single handed GP surgeries

Covering a single handed practices has its own set of problems:

- You will be the only doctor there, so you will need to deal with issues that many locums would pass over to, or at least discuss with, the patients' usual doctor.

- You won't be able to limit your workload by 'clocking off' and leaving things to the principals. This can mean a lot of extra work if things get busy.

- You will need to do repeat prescribing and results management for patients that you have not dealt with, which can be avoided in larger practices. This increases the workload and medico-legal risk.

- You will need to do visits, which can he avoided in larger practices.

- You will usually need to provide on call cover during the day (eg: 8.30am until 6.30pm)

- You may need to run the dispensary as well if it is a dispensing practice.

These factors need to be taken into account when negotiating rates for single handed practices. Make sure that your rate is adequate, and that your terms and conditions allow for variations in workload that can occur.

The Office of Fair Trading and the setting of locum rates

The BMA used to publish recommended GP locum rates which were used across the UK. Then in 1999 the Office of Fair Trading (OFT) decided that this breached the Competition Act 1998.

In the United Kingdom, the Competition Act 1998 is designed to make sure that businesses compete on a level footing. It does so by prohibiting certain types of anti-competitive behaviour, such as the formation of cartels.

In its simplest terms, a cartel is an agreement between businesses (called *undertakings*) not to compete with each other on, amongst other things, price. The agreement is usually verbal and often informal. The OFT has strong powers to investigate businesses suspected of breaching the Act and to impose tough penalties on those that do[*].

Caution:

Some local locum groups, GP co-ops, and LMCs have continued to publish suggested locum rates since 1999.

However, the publishing of suggested locum rates by these groups is also considered to be a breach of the Competition Act, and recently one urban locum group retracted its recommended rates after a locum threatened to refer them to the OFT. Locum rates in the city subsequently rose by up to 35%, which confirmed the suspicion that this behaviour was suppressing locum rates.

Since the BMA rate was prohibited, some GPs and locums have simply added the Dentist and Doctors Pay Review Body pay awards to the old rates, and a few have even stuck to the old 1999 BMA rates and have not had a pay rise since 1999.

---

[*] Up to 10% of their turnover, backdated for up to three years, or even an unlimited fine and a prison sentences of up to five years.

Note:

Primary Care Organisations (PCOs) are not classed as undertakings by the OFT. This has produced the perverse situation that PCOs can collude with each other as much as they like over rates and fees, but the doctors that they are dealing with cannot.

Travel expenses

Most locums invoice units for at least some of their travel costs. These can include:

- Return vehicle mileage from your home to the unit where you are providing cover.

- Visit mileage while working at the practice (see below for setting of vehicle rates

- Other mileage, such as to and from your accommodation (eg: self catering accommodation for a remote practice).

- Public transport costs, flights, ferry tickets, and car hire costs are possible expenses for long distance locums.

> *Note:*
>
> Charging mileage between your home and the practice causes confusion with many principals (and even locums).
>
> If you are a partner/salaried GP then you cannot claim mileage to/from your home to your practice as business miles for tax purposes. This is because the practice is considered your normal place of work.
>
> However, as a self-employed locum your place of business is usually your home office, so travel mileage between the practice (your customer) and your home (your place of business) is a legitimate business expense for which you can charge a fee and claim as an expense for tax purposes.

Setting a vehicle mileage rate

The standard HM Revenue and Customs business rate for 2005 is 40p/mile for the first 10,000 miles and then 25p per mile thereafter[*].

However, HM Revenue and Customs rates do not apply to self-employed locums, and you can set any rate that you like (assuming you can find a practice that will pay it). Average rates tend to vary from 25p/mile to 60p/mile. However, it is important to set a rate that will at least return the actual costs of running your car.

To find out an estimate of how much your vehicle costs to run per mile you can look in the tables that are found at the back of most popular automobile magazines. You can also calculate your costs by:

1. Adding up all your set vehicle costs (depreciation in that year, insurance, repairs/servicing, road tax).

---

[*] Rates vary depending on engine size and total mileage.

See http://www.hmrc.gov.uk/rates/travel.htm

2. Divide this cost by the number of miles you expect to drive in that year.

3. Work out your average fuel cost per mile by dividing the cost of a gallon of petrol (there are 4.4 litres per UK gallon) by the number of miles you car does per gallon (official figures should be listed in your vehicle manual). For example, if a litre of fuel costs 80p, then a gallon costs 4.4 x 80 = £3.52, and if your vehicle is listed as having an average fuel consumption of 30mpg, then the average cost per mile should be just under 12p per mile (£3.52 / 30).

4. You can also work out your average fuel cost per mile by filling up your fuel tank, zeroing your trip indicator, and then the next time you fill your tank divide the cost of your fuel by the number of miles travelled since you last filled your tank. For example, if you travelled 200 miles from a full tank and then put in £20 of fuel to refill your tank, then your average cost per mile is 10p (£20 / 200 miles).

5. Add the cost per mile for fuel (3 or 4 above) to the cost per mile for the standing costs from (1 above) for your total cost per mile.

Although you should avoid charging less than the actual cost of your vehicle mileage, you can charge more than this for mileage. If you are travelling a long way to work, then you may want to make a profit to cover the time you are spending in your car (unless you are charging a practice for the time you spend travelling, which is unusual).

Tip:

The above calculations are based on average cost per mile.

However, since you are already paying the fixed costs anyway, the additional cost of extra miles that you do is less than the average cost (because the more miles that you drive, the less the average cost per mile).

So, you can also calculate mileage costs as just those that you incur from doing more miles than you otherwise would (i.e.: the fuel cost per mile, the cost of having to service your vehicle more often, and the extra depreciation for a higher mileage car).

Discounting work

Should I offer a discount for some types of work?

Some locums discount their rate for some of the following:

- Quiet units with low work intensity

- Low intensity on call work

- Quiet times of year (eg: January and February)

However, few locums would discount their rate for:

- Short notice bookings – since it is more difficult for units to find locums cover at short notice, you could argue that a surcharge would be more appropriate.

- Long term bookings – this does have some advantages for locums (you don't have to move around as much etc.), but it also has advantages for the unit booking cover (they don't have to spend time finding lots of different locums, and don't have the risk of not finding locum cover). There are also some disadvantages for locums – you may get drawn into providing more administration and chronic illness support.

Many locums consider that they are being paid for their time whether it is quiet or not, and so do not discount at all.

Should I offer a discount if it's a quiet surgery?

If you are booked for a surgery, but when you turn up there are lots of empty slots, then you have several options. Bear in mind that it is the practice's responsibility to ensure that you are utilised properly, and it is not your fault that their surgery is quiet. It is very unlikely that you will be able to find other work for the same period, and you should not be disadvantaged by something that is not your fault.

Your options are:

- Chill out during the quiet period and bill the practice for the hours booked (make sure your cancellation clause is in your terms and conditions).

- Do other work for them (such as a visit, or routine paperwork, should you be willing to do this type of work). Or, you could make the staff a cup of coffee, which is always a good way to win friends.

- If you would prefer to go home instead, then you could offer to finish early and not charge for the unused period.

Private Work

The rates section above, and the rates that most locum charge, are for NHS work. Most locums would say that private work should not be included in your standard rate.

Some practices argue that the extra cost of private work is to cover the overheads, but this argument is overstated. At most, overheads for such work will be 25% (excluding any marketing costs for the service, which are rare in health care). Also, most of these overheads are fixed (ie: the practice would need to pay these overheads whether the extra work is carried out or not). The differential between what the locum will be paid (NHS locum rate) and what the practice will receive for essentially doing very little (about 2-3x what the locum will receive) is extreme. Many locums would consider this exploitation, which is why they insist that private fees be negotiated separately.

Private work in NHS units usually consists of medical certificates, medical reports, insurance examinations, or licensing examinations. The reasons why higher fees are charged include:

- The work is often tedious and unpopular.

- Private fees reflect the actual worth of the doctor's time much more accurately than NHS fees (the NHS uses its monopoly provider position to keep fees down).

- There are higher medico-legal risks for this work (as much of it involves insurance claims or legal process).

If a unit does insist on keeping private fees, then you should consider how much private work will be involved and whether you could earn more by doing less private work somewhere else. One option is to charge a higher standard locum rate to take account of any private work involved.

Other points about private fees:

- The rates for private work are much higher than for NHS work (about three times as high on average).

- When charging separately for private work, then the time taken for the private work should not be included in the NHS locum fee (except for work carried out when on call).

- Most locums suggest that any private fees payable should go direct to the locum, however, the practice may want a percentage for their overheads - usually about 10 to 20% (remember you have overheads as well).

- Rates for various items of private work are published in the magazine Medeconomics, but don't be afraid to charge more (or less) for the ones that are negotiable.

Locum income examples

The following tables show what level of income can be expected based on various work intensities and hourly rates.

Workload

Before we can work out income, we need to work out how much time you are going to be spending actually at work earning money. So let's assume that you are planning to take four weeks per year holiday, a couple of weeks study leave and on average you will miss one week per year from unpaid illness.

We then throw in an average travel cost to and from sessions based on the number of sessions worked.

Table 1.

Holiday	4	Wks/yr
Study leave	2	Wks/yr
Sick leave	1	Wks/yr
Paid work	45	Wks/yr
Session Length	3.5	hours
Vehicle cost	£0.50	/mile
Avg distance	5	miles
Admin/travel	1	sess/wk

Expenses

Once we know the workload, we need to work out what expenses you are going to incur. We can't work out how much profit you are going to make until we know how much the expenses are. The travel expenses are based on the travel distances we listed in table 1 above.

Table 2.

Expenses	Per session	Annual
Indemnity		£3,500
Travel/Vehicle	£5.00	
Office/Computer/Mobile		£2,000
Equipment/Drugs		£500
BMA/GMC etc		£1,000
Study costs		£1,000

Income

Now that we know the workload and expenses, we can calculate an annual income.

Table 3 shows the income based on working an average of seven sessions per week (excluding an eighth admin session).

Table 3 Seven sessions per week (plus one admin session)

Rate/hr	£/session	Turnover	Expenses	Profit
£35	£123	£38,745	£9,575	£29,170
£45	£158	£49,770	£9,575	£40,195
£55	£193	£60,795	£9,575	£51,220
£65	£228	£71,820	£9,575	£62,245
£75	£263	£82,845	£9,575	£73,270
£85	£298	£93,870	£9,575	£84,295

> *Tip:*
> You can download and play with a working version of the spreadsheet that these tables are based on (in excel® format) from the locum123.com website[*].

Table 4 shows the income based on the heavier schedule of nine sessions per week (excluding a tenth admin session). It can be difficult for locums to consistently organise nine sessions per week.

---

[*] http://www.locum123.com/survival_pack.shtml

Table 4. Nine sessions per week (plus one admin session)

Rate/hr	£/session	Turnover	Expenses	Profit
£35	£123	£49,815	£10,025	£39,790
£45	£158	£63,990	£10,025	£53,965
£55	£193	£78,165	£10,025	£68,140
£65	£228	£92,340	£10,025	£82,315
£75	£263	£106,515	£10,025	£96,490
£85	£298	£120,690	£10,025	£110,665

Average GP income in 2005 was around £100,000 per year in England, so you can see that a GP locum will need to work 10 sessions per week (including one admin session) at £75 per hour with minimal expenses to approach an average GP income.

Notes for locum income example table:

- Expenses vary - this example is a low estimate based on a locum that does not work away from home.

- Indemnity rates vary by company - the included rate is an estimate

- Vehicle expenses are based on an full size family car owned from new (50p/mile)

- Profit calculation excludes any charges for visit mileage etc..

- Profit shown is pre-tax and does not include superannuation, national insurance or tax.

- For comparison, the old 1999 BMA rate was £33.50 per hour.

Chapter 5:
Terms and Conditions, Bookings, and Invoices

It is important to define what your duties will be when you are working for a practice, as this varies considerably. This will make your agreement more transparent, and will help avoid misunderstandings and disagreements.

Once the terms have been agreed, you will need to confirm your booking and later issue an invoice for the work done so that you get paid.

Specifying which duties you will perform

Normally, the duties that you may be asked to carry out will include:

- Face to face consultations
- Telephone consultations
- Home visits
- Results handling/Routine paperwork

- Repeat prescriptions
- On call / Emergency cover / Duty doctor

You may want to limit which of these duties you perform – for example, some locums avoid doing visits or routine results/prescriptions because these present problems for locum doctors who don't know the area or the patients.

Face to face consultations

This makes up the bulk of most routine locum GP work.

You should specify:

- How quickly you are prepared to see patients (eg: 10 minute consultations).

- What breaks you require, if any (eg: one 10 minute 'catch up/paperwork slot' every hour).

- How many patients you are willing to see per hour (eg: maximum 5 patients per hour)

- How many patients you are willing to see in a single session (eg: maximum 18 patients per session).

- How much 'clean up time' you expect at the end of a surgery (many locums add 30 minutes to the end of a surgery to handle paperwork from the consultations).

- What penalties, if any, you will impose for seeing more patients than this (eg: extra patients seen during this period be charged at $1/5^{th}$ of the standard hourly rate).

Remember that to operate safely a locum often requires more time in the consultation than someone who knows the practice and the patients.

Telephone consultations

These are common in general practice locum work. They include telephone triage of visits, telephone triage of consultation requests, calls regarding results, and giving advice to patients by telephone.

You may wish to set separate terms for telephone consultations, although many locums simply use the same terms as for face to face consultations.

Home visits

Visiting unknown patients, in an area that may be unfamiliar to you, is more risky medico-legally than for a principal who knows the patients and the area.

It takes locums longer to carry out home visits, and while many practices are very helpful as regards leaving more time for visits, supplying maps and directions etc., some are not. As a result, quite a few locums feel that visiting is not an efficient use of their time, and are not willing to do home visits. Many of the locums that do visits, charge a 'per visit' fee (either on top of, or instead of, an hourly rate*).

You should specify:

- Whether you are willing to do home visits or not for this practice.

- That home visits take longer for locums and are more medico-legally risky than for principals that know the patients/area.

- Whether there will be a supplementary charge for home visits.

- If there is a limit on how many visits you are willing to do per day (this can be tricky, as distances for visits vary).

- If there is a limit on how many visits you are able to per hour (again, this can be tricky, as distances for visits vary).

Routine paperwork/results

Handling results and routine paperwork, on patients that are not known to you (ie: results and letters for patients that you have not seen in consultations or on visits), carries a higher medico-legal risk, and you should consider avoiding this if possible.

---

* See Chapter 4: Setting Locum Rates.

MDU advice is that the notes should be supplied and checked for every result looked at by a locum. This is time consuming, and (as with home visits) many locums feel this is not an efficient use of their time and are not willing to accept the risks involved.

You should specify in your terms:

- Whether you are willing to do routine paperwork or not for this practice.

- That routine paperwork take longer for locums, and is more medico-legally risky than for doctors that know the patients.

- Whether there will be a supplementary charge for this work.

Routine repeat prescribing

Carrying out repeat prescribing for patients that you have not seen in surgery/on home visits, is similar to routine paperwork. It is higher risk, and more time consuming work.

MDU again advises that the notes should be checked for every prescription signed no matter what system for repeat prescribing is in use. This makes the for very time consuming work, and, again, many locums are not willing to accept the risk and feel it is not efficient for them to do this kind of work.

Tip:

Some locums ask the practice to certify in writing that the repeat prescribing system is safe and that it is subjected to regular audit to ensure that it is robust.

Again, you should specify in your terms:

- Whether you are willing to do routine repeat prescribing or not for this practice.

- That repeat prescribing take longer for locums, and is more medico-legally risky than for doctors that know the patients.

- Whether there will be a supplementary charge for this work.

Payment terms

You should make your payment terms clear in advance.

Many locums insist on payment by cheque on completion of the locum work, or at the end of set periods for longer bookings (eg: weekly). Payment in advance is rare, but should be strongly considered if there are any doubts about the financial viability of the unit being covered (eg: a partnership that is in crisis, or is having financial problems).

If you offer credit, then you should specify when payment is expected by, and any penalties for late payment (see late payment section below).

Cancellation clause

You should decide what your policy on locum cancellations is going to be. If a unit cancels a booking, how much notice will you require? If they cancel at short notice, how much compensation will you want?

One policy is to charge a 100% cancellation fee if they give less than 1-2 months notice. Other locums charge a sliding scale for cancellations (eg: 100% for less than 1 month notice, 50% for less than 2 months notice). Some locums only apply the cancellation fee if other suitable work cannot be arranged easily.

Accommodation

If you are working away from home, you should decide how you are going to fund your accommodation and subsistence costs. These can be significant (up to £100 per day in some cases).

Possible costs include:

- Self catering accommodation
- Motel or hotel accommodation
- Eating out (if not self-catering)
- Extra costs for calls from mobile phone
- Internet access
- Mail forwarding

You may want to include these costs in your normal rates, or you may prefer to charge a separate fee for them. Alternatively, you can ask the practice to arrange and pay for your accommodation directly. In this case, you should consider setting terms regarding minimum standards for accommodation, and that you reserve the right to ask for alternative accommodation if there is a problem.

> *Example:*
>
> I've slept on a mattress on a coffee room floor before, and had some pretty awful accommodation provided for me in the past, which can really sap your enthusiasm for the job.

Chaperones

Locums are particularly vulnerable to complaints because they work in unfamiliar environments with unfamiliar patients. This is compounded by the fact that practice policies vary, and locums often have to alter their own consulting style to 'fit in'.

You should consider including a clause in your terms and conditions about provision of chaperones for intimate examinations. Recent legal cases, and advice from the GMC and RCGP on the issue of chaperones, should be considered.

You may want to bear in mind:

- GMC advice is that a chaperone should be offered for every intimate examination. (should you choose to proceed without a chaperone, you should record that a chaperone was offered and declined in the notes).

- Many practices use receptionists as chaperones (the receptionist being present in the room, but separated from the examiner and patient by a curtain). This practice is considered inadequate by the MPS and RCGP patient-partnership, who recommend the use of a member of the clinical team.

- Many practices use patients' relatives as chaperones. This has problems too, and may not offer an adequate defence against misunderstandings and malicious complaints.

- Some practices are unwilling to provide a nurse chaperone.

- Some practice do not use chaperones for same-sex examinations.

Including a clear chaperone provision clause in you terms and conditions will clarify your position for practices, will help avoid problems 'on the day', and will strengthen your position if you are unwilling to examine because there is inadequate chaperone provision by the practice, and the patient complains about a delay in examination.

Other items

You may want to specify other conditions, such as:

- Handling of complaints[*].
- Fees for private work[†].

Examples of GP Terms and Conditions

You can see examples of Terms and Conditions in the Quotation and Confirmation Form template (Appendix C) – copies of which are available to download in word format from the locum123.com website[‡].

Confirming locum bookings

Once you have agreed rates and terms, it is advisable to send the practice a written confirmation/quote for the work that you plan to do.

You should include:

- Dates and times of cover.
- Duties involved (and those not involved).
- The total cost of the locum cover (with a list of any supplementary charge items if appropriate).

---

[*] See Chapter 12: Clinical Aspects: complaints

[†] See Chapter 4: Setting Locum Rates

[‡] You can download copies of the templates from:
http://www.locum123.com/survival_pack.html

- Your terms and conditions of work.

- Any travelling / accommodation / subsistence expenses that you expect them to meet.

It is wise to request that they confirm acceptance of this in writing by post, fax, or email. The easiest way to achieve this is to email them a copy of your quote (complete with your terms and conditions) and ask them to reply saying that this is acceptable (and that the dates/times are correct). Alternatively, you can fax them a copy and ask them to sign and date the document and fax it back to you.

Tip:

When emailing documents, it is probably better to use an Adobe Acrobat® (.pdf) file rather than a Microsoft Word® (or .doc) file. The advantages are that a pdf file will appear the same on any computer, and cannot be altered by the recipient. The disadvantage is that some IT-poor practices might struggle to read a pdf file (although they are pretty universal these days).

If you use a Mac, you can print your word documents directly to a pdf file.

You may want to include a clause that you will automatically cancel the booking if you do not receive their confirmation within a set time period (eg: 1 week). However, this has the disadvantage that, if their reply is lost, you may cancel work that they think has been confirmed.

Invoicing practices

Issuing invoices

At the end of each locum period, you should issue an invoice to the practice. The invoice should contain the date, the period of cover and an itemised list of services provided with the total amount due at the bottom.

It should also contain a list of payment options. This is normally simply the name that the cheque should be made out to, but you can include your bank details to allow practices to pay by BACS[*].

In most cases, locums hand practices their invoice at the end of the locum period and leave with a cheque in their hand. However, in some cases the practice may be unable to supply a cheque. For example, the person required to countersign the cheque may not be available, or the payment may be coming directly from a Primary Care Organisation.

What is a suitable locum period for invoicing?

A locum period is anything you want it to be, and can be as short as a one-hour surgery, or as long as a three month long term locum. Usually, it is at the end of each booking, or one to two weeks for longer bookings.

For most locums, cash flow becomes an issue if they are not paid for more than four weeks or so, and there is always the very remote, but serious, risk that the practice will dissolve or become bankrupt before you are paid.

Sample Invoice

The following sample invoice shows one common format for locum invoices. It lists the locum period being billed, the rate and number of items (two days at £500 per day), and the payment methods and credit terms (cheques or BACS within 28 days).

---

[*] BACS is the Banking Automated Clearing Service. It's a form of electronic payment in which a business can transfer funds from their account to a third party's account electronically.

2nd June, 2005   Dr Lorna Locum

                                        33 Locum Drive

Practice Manager   Anytown

Anytown Practice   AA2 1AB

North Road   Tel. 01234 567890

Anytown

AA1 2BC

Dear Practice Manager,

Re: Invoice for locum cover

Dates: 01.06.2005 - 02.06.2005

Item	Rate	Number	Sub-total
Full days	£500	2	£1000
		TOTAL	**£1000**

Please make cheques payable to 'Dr Lorna Locum'

BACS payment can be made to:

Account Name: Dr Lorna Locum

Sort Code: 99-11-01

Account Number: 12345678

Please note that payment is due within 28 days of the invoice date, and that there is a 5% surcharge for late payment.

Yours sincerely,

DR LORNA LOCUM

Anecdote:

On being booked for one locum, I found the practice in some disarray with one of the principals having left suddenly without explanation. It transpired that the principal was the financial brains of the practice, which did not have a partnership agreement, I became concerned, and discussed with the remaining partners the possibility of being paid in advance. The practice dissolved a short time after I left. Had I not already been paid, it was possible that the individual partners might have disagreed as to who was to pay me. Without a formal partnership agreement, I could have been left chasing payment for some time without any guarantee of success.

Accepting payments by debit or credit card

It is now quite simple to offer to take payments by credit card via Paypal™*, as anyone with an email address can receive online payments via Paypal™.

If you register your details online at the Paypal™ website, you can then transfer any payments received into your bank account (or you can use them to make purchases via Paypal™). This can also be useful for accepting private fees from patients, who occasionally ask 'do you take visa?'.

A payment can be made by visiting the Paypal™ website and clicking on 'Send Money' at the top of the home page (it is necessary to register online first). The payee can then enter the recipient's email address and the amount to pay by debit or credit card.

---

* http://www.paypal.com

Of course, credit card charges make this method of payment unattractive for large sums of money, but it can be useful for small fees.

Late payment

Many PCOs, and occasionally practices, can take a long time to pay invoices. So it is wise to include a late payment surcharge in your agreement, and to restate this surcharge in your invoice. This will allow you to recover any costs of having to borrow to make up any shortfall in your cash flow from late payment.

Charging interest and penalties for late payment is covered by the Late Payment of Commercial Debts (Interest) Act 1998. This allows you to charge interest at 8% above the Bank of England interest rate and applies even when no payment terms have been agreed. The default terms (used if you do not issue formal terms yourself) are payment within 28 days of the date of issue of the invoice.

Tip:

To calculate the interest due multiply the outstanding amount by the interest rate and then divide by 365 to get the daily interest. Multiply by the number of days late the invoice is to get the total amount due.

When it comes to other penalties for late payment, you can state hefty penalties in your terms, but the law is that the penalty must accurately reflect the costs incurred. So unless you suffered bank charges due to cash flow problems from late payment, you may have problems enforcing penalty clauses.

Of course, unless the amount is significant, it is often better to waive late fees in the interest of 'customer relations'. This is especially true if the practice pays by return of post when reminded. Late fees can damage your relationship with a practice.

Anecdote:

Whilst away for a few weeks doing locum work, my wife received a telephone call from a company to say that one of our direct debits had bounced. It transpired that the health board we had been working for had not paid us, and the invoice for around £8,000 was several weeks overdue. This had resulted in our account going into unauthorised overdraft, and the bank had begun to bounce our direct debits.

My wife was with The Royal Bank of Scotland at the time, and they had a policy of not taking any steps to inform customers when their accounts became overdrawn[*]

The Royal Bank of Scotland charged us around £600 in fees for this episode.

We have since moved to First Direct bank, for whom we have no limit of admiration (not least because they send us daily SMS text messages with our current balance).

Fortunately the 10% late payment surcharge covered the bank fees.

Non-payment

This is thankfully quite rare in the NHS (late payment being much more common).

---

[*] Actually, the Royal Bank of Scotland did inform its customers the FIRST time they became overdrawn. But only the first time. My wife had become a few pounds overdrawn some months or years earlier by accident, and so the bank took no steps to inform us of the problem on this subsequent occasion.

You should initially send another invoice marked 'overdue' in red ink, with any late payment surcharge that might apply. You may want to offer to ignore the late payment surcharge/interest if payment is received within a certain period of time (eg: 7 days). You should send the reminder recorded delivery. Check that the letter is recorded as having been received[*].

If you still do not receive payment, then call the practice manager and, if necessary, send a final reminder marked 'final reminder' in red ink (again, using recorded delivery).

In the unusual event that you should continue to have problems with non-payment despite reminder invoices, then you can contact the BMA local office, or a solicitor, for advice. You can, for example, take the unit to the Small Claims Court.

You can report failure to pay to the local PCO, and, in extreme cases where a doctor has acted improperly in financial dealings with a colleague, the GMC may take an interest. It may be worth pointing this out to a practice where payment is very overdue.

---

[*] You can do this online via the Royal Mail website: http://www.royalmail.com

Chapter 6:
Tax and National Insurance

Introduction to tax and National Insurance

"But in this world nothing can be said to be certain, except death and taxes." -Benjamin Franklin, Writings Vol. x "Letter to Jean Baptiste Le Roy"

Sadly we must pay tax on the income we earn. Of course these taxes are essential, in that they pay for the wonders of a modern society, but it still hurts when you sign the cheque.

This chapter discusses the common tax payment methods (PAYE and Schedule D) as well as VAT and National Insurance contributions (which are supposed to pay for the NHS).

Pay As You Earn (PAYE)

Employee locums will be put through the PAYE system. This mainly applies to hospital locums employed by NHS trusts/Health Boards directly or via a locum agency, but it may also apply to GP locums in some circumstances. Some out of hours providers employ GPs for sessions through PAYE, for example, and GP locums who use a limited company may be employees of that company.

In PAYE, your employer removes your tax and other contributions (pension, national insurance) from your salary each month. The money you are paid is therefore 'net' (ie: you won't have to pay tax on it later).

Although you are PAYE, you should still submit a tax return at the end of the tax year if you have earned other income (that was not taxed as PAYE, for example cremation fees), or if you want to receive a refund for your expenses.

The advantages of PAYE are that it is simple and hassle free. The disadvantages are that there are fewer allowable expenses that you can put against tax, and you can't spread your tax liability with your spouse (see below).

Example:

Lorna Locum takes a salaried OOH post with her local PCT. She earns £50,000 before tax, but £15,000 is deducted at source as PAYE tax.

However, Lorna's income includes a car allowance (which is taxed) and she pays her own GMC and indemnity fees.

Lorna submits a tax return listing her business vehicle mileage costs and GMC/indemnity fees as legitimate business expenses[*]. These expenses come to £6000. So, as she earns enough to be in the 40% tax bracket, Lorna will receive back £2400 of the tax she has paid to HM Revenue and Customs (40% of £6000).

---

[*] see Chapter 7: Business expenses

Schedule D (Self employed)

GPs in the UK are classed as being self-employed, and are taxed under Schedule D. This means that, like any other self-employed small business person, they do not pay tax as they go along (PAYE). Instead, they keep a record of all of their income (turnover), and all of their expenses.

At the end of each tax year they total these up to produce an overall profit for the year (turnover minus expenses) and they then submit a tax return and pay tax on this profit.

The main advantage of being a Schedule D tax payer is the more liberal allowance of expenses. This is because employees should have pretty much everything they need provided for them by their employer, but small businesspeople need to provide all these things for themselves.

VAT

VAT stands for Value Added Tax. This is a tax that is added at the point of sale of VAT rated goods and services in the UK. Businesses only have to register for VAT purposes if their turnover of VAT rated goods or services is greater than £58,000 per year. Businesses below this level can voluntarily register for VAT purposes as there can be advantages (such as recouping the cost of VAT paid on any business expenses), however it is highly unlikely that this would be of any advantage to a locum GP.

Locum work is not currently VAT rated, so there is no need for locums to register for VAT purposes, nor for locums to charge VAT on their invoices.

Some medical work is VAT rated – such as private medical reports for insurance companies. However, it is unlikely that a locum GP will earn enough from such work to be required to become VAT registered.

Tax on dividend income

If you are receiving dividends from shares that you own in limited companies, unit trusts, or open-ended investment companies, then this is taxed separately.

Dividend tax is a bit complicated, and is largely outside the scope of this book. It involved a separate tax on the dividends, which includes a tax credit that you can use against income tax.

The final result is that dividends are essentially tax-free until you reach the higher tax rate bracket (£32,400 in 2005/6). Once you earn above this amount, dividends are taxed at around 22.5%.

This will affect you if you are working through your own limited company and paying yourself partly (or mostly) with dividends[*].

Corporation Tax

If you are working through your own limited company, then your company will pay Corporation Tax on all of its profits (turnover minus expenses), and you will pay personal tax on the salary and dividends that you receive from the company.

In 2005/6, companies that have a profit of less than £10,000 per year don't pay any corporation tax, while companies with a profit of over £50,000 pay a rate of 19%[†]. If your profit falls between £10,000 and £50,000 things are a bit more complicated (but will lie somewhere between 0% and 19% depending on the profit). However, 'husband and wife' companies now pay 19% corporation tax on all profits below £300,000 – you should discuss the implications of this with your accountant.

---

[*] See Chapter 3: Running your own business for more details on limited companies.

[†] If your company is lucky enough to have a profit of over £300,000 per year, then it will be liable to a higher rate of corporation tax.

How tax is calculated

Your tax is based on your income. For tax purposes your income is essentially your profit for the tax year. That is, your turnover (the total amount you got paid) minus your expenses (the total amount you paid for things that you use to provide your service).

You pay varying amounts of tax on the different bands of your income. You have a tax-free personal allowance (£4895 in 2005/6), then the starting rate, basic rate, and higher rate tax bands.

UK Tax Rates 2005/6

Tax Rates 2005/6	Rate	Band
Personal allowance	0%	£4895
Starting rate	10%	£0 to £2090
Basic rate	22%	£2090 to £32,400
Higher rate	40%	Over £32,400

Tip:

The locum123.com Locum Income and Tax Calculator.is a useful online assistant that can help you gain a rough estimate of your tax liability.

Example:

Lorna Locum received £65,000 for all of her locum work, private fees, and other income between April 2004 and April 2005. Her **turnover** was therefore £65,000.

During the same period she spent £10,000 on **expenses** such as her car*, computers†, medical indemnity, education, GMC fees, and so on. So her **profit** was £55,000 for the year (£65,000 minus £10,000). Her income for tax purposes was therefore £55,000 (ie: her profit).

This is then compared to the tax allowances for that tax year. For example, if her tax-free band was £5000, then she would not pay tax on the first £5000 of profit.

Her taxable income is therefore £50,000 (£55,000 profit minus £5,000 personal allowance). If the starting rate tax was 10% of her taxable income up to £5,000, and the basic rate tax was 20% of that income up to £30,000, and higher rate tax was 50% of any remaining income over £30,000, then Lorna would be liable for £15,500 in tax (10% of the first £5,000 = £500, 25% of the next £25,000 = £5,000 tax, and 50% of the final £20,000 = £10,000)‡.

So from a turnover of £60,000, Lorna only gets to keep £34.500 (£10,000 goes on expenses, and £15,500 goes on tax).

You can see how important it is to claim for appropriate expenses, because if Lorna had not done so, then she would have paid an extra £5,000 in tax (50% of £10,000).

---

* Business mileage proportion of her car use – see Chapter 7: Business Expenses

† Business proportion of her computer use – see Chapter 7: Business Expenses

‡ This example has been simplified to make the figures easier – you can find out the current UK tax bands and tax rates from the HM Revenue and Customs website, or from your accountant.

http://www.hmrc.gov.uk

National Insurance

There are two classes of NI contribution that apply to locums:

1. Class 2 contributions: these are flat rate payments, a few pounds a week, that enable you to receive Incapacity Benefit, Maternity pay, State Pension etc.. They are usually collected monthly or quarterly by direct debit. You can arrange to pay these by contacting you local HM Revenue and Customs office[*].

2. Class 4 contributions: these are collected as part of your tax return at the end of each tax year. They apply to a percentage of income over a certain threshold, and have a capped upper limit.

If you have a limited company, and take part of the profits out of the company via dividends, then those dividend payments do not currently attract NI contributions.

Putting money aside for tax

When you are self-employed, then you need to put money aside for your tax bill as you go, otherwise you will have problems when you tax bill becomes due.

It is best to put this money into a high interest savings account, but you can also use it to pay off debt such as car HP, loans, or credit cards during the year. This will save you money on interest payments (as you will earn far less in a savings account than you will pay for a loan), but bear in mind that you will need to re-borrow most of this money when your tax bill is due.

You can use this money to set against an offset mortgage, but bear in mind that the higher interest rate on such a mortgage will often cancel out any potential savings, and may cost you more in the end.

---

[*] which can be found online at http://www.hmrc.gov.uk/enq/index.htm

Putting away 33% of your profit is a good rule of thumb, but it is worth finding a good medical accountant to advise you on how best to plan for your tax bill (see below).

Annual tax returns

The personal tax year runs from April to April. Once you have notified the HM Revenue and Customs that you are now self-employed[*], they will send you a tax form after April.

You then need to prepare and submit your tax return (including your payment) by the end of January the following year.

When you submit your first tax return, you will be asked to pay the tax due for the year just ended, as well as 50% of the estimate for next year's tax 'in advance'. The other 50% is due at the end of July of the same year.

The estimate for tax to be paid in advance is based solely on your tax bill from the previous year. Should your actual tax for the year differ from the estimated tax that you have already paid, then you will receive a refund or you will be required to pay the difference. If you expect your income to change significantly, then you can ask your accountant to submit a different estimate.

It's wise to submit your return as early as possible, and to pay your tax on time. There are penalties for late payment.

---

[*] Remember that if you don't inform HM Revenue and Customs within three months of becoming self-employed they may fine you £100.

Accountants

You can use the Locum Income and Tax Calculator[*] on the locum123.com website to estimate your annual expenses and tax liability. However, this is no substitute for professional accountancy advice.

Accountants usually charge around £200 to prepare a single year of tax accounts for a self-employed locum GP. However, this fee varies between accountants. Also, if you burn them a CD of your Quicken™ accounts with all your expenses correctly filed, then you should be paying less than if you give your accountant several shoeboxes full of invoices and say 'see what you can make of these'.

GP finances are complex, and it is essential that you have an accountant that is experienced in handling GP accounts. Ask around the practices in your area to see who they use.

Tax avoidance and tax evasion

Understanding the difference between tax avoidance and tax evasion is vital if you are self-employed or a small businessperson.

Tax avoidance

Steps to minimise your tax burden within the law are called 'tax avoidance'. Tax avoidance is legal, it is common business practice, and it can result in significant savings.

Basically, tax avoidance means understanding how the tax system works and running your business in the most tax efficient way possible.

---

[*] http://www.locum123.com/calculator.cgi

Example:

It's March. In May you are planning to buy a new computer which you will use only for work. The computer costs £2,000,

However, your accountant has sent you a leaflet explaining that the current rule allowing 100% of IT capital purchases (which would include your computer) to be claimed in the same tax year will end this year.

Since May is at the start of the next tax year, if you wait until then to buy your computer, you will only get to claim 25% of the value (£500) in that tax year.

However, if you buy the computer now, then you can include the expense in this tax year's accounts, and you will be able to claim 100% (£2,000) towards this year's tax.

As you are a 40% tax payer, this will mean £800 off this year's tax bill which is due in January (40% of £2,000) compared with £200 off next year's tax bill the following January.

Buying the computer now instead of later is a good example of sensible tax avoidance.

An experienced, specialised medical accountant is the best source of advice on how to avoid paying unnecessary tax.

Tax evasion

Tax evasion is completely different from tax avoidance. Tax evasion is illegally attempting to reduce your tax burden.

For example, not declaring some of your income to avoid paying tax on it is tax evasion. This is most commonly seen with cash payments, which are difficult for HM Revenue and Customs to trace. This is sometimes referred to as 'being paid under the table'.

Another example would be employing your spouse for work that he or she did not do solely to spread your tax burden and pay less tax.

Tax evasion is a criminal offence which can result in a jail sentence, and should therefore be considered 'A Very Bad Thing.'.

If you are concerned about the difference between tax evasion and tax avoidance, speak to an experienced, specialised medical accountant.

Chapter 7:
Business Expenses

Introduction to business expenses

From the point of view of expenses, running your own business has two significant differences from being employed.

- You will incur extra new expenses that you would not have had as an employee.

- You can claim more legitimate expenses on things that you could not class as expenses when you were employed.

It is vital to identify and document all of your legitimate expenses, because they reduce your tax bill. As a rule of thumb, anything that you use that helps you generate increased turnover is a legitimate expense.

In this chapter, we will be looking at some common business expenses, and some common expenses that are not allowed as tax deductions.

> *Important:*
>
> Assuming that you are earning enough money to be paying tax in the higher tax rate (which for 2005/6 is 40% of taxable income over £32,400), then every pound of expenditure that you can justify as being an allowable tax deduction will reduce your tax bill by 40p.
>
> So, if you are sloppy and don't bother much with recording your expenses, and you fail to declare say £5,000 of expenses, then you will pay an extra £2,000 in unnecessary tax.
>
> Worse still, since you have already spent that £5,000 on other things (ie: the expenses), you will need to earn more to pay the extra £2,000 in tax. And since you will also be taxed on the extra money needed to pay the original tax bill, you will really be losing £3300 (the original £2,000 tax plus 40% tax on top for the £2,,000 of extra earnings needed to pay the tax).
>
> So, it's absolutely vital that you record your expenses properly.

Common allowable tax deductions

Office expenses

You can claim all of your purchases of paper, postage costs, envelopes, rubber stamps, and so on, as legitimate business expenses.

You can also claim a portion of your home expenses (mortgage/rent, rates and utilities) if you use part of your home as an office. Although this appears tempting at first glance, there is a problem with this when you come to sell your house. Assuming the value of your home has gone up, HM Revenue and Customs will want to tax you on a proportion of the rise in value based on the proportion of the property that you claimed was business. So, if you are a home owner, it is probably best to claim just a proportion of your utility bills and rates, and not your mortgage.

Computer expenses

A business needs computers, printers, printer cartridges and so on to function efficiently. However, there are two things to bear in mind when claiming computer expenses.

Firstly, once you calculate the total cost of all your computer expenses (games aside!), you should then decide on what proportion of the computer should be considered as business use.

For example, if you use the computer half the time for business, and half the time for other things, then you should count 50% of the costs towards tax. This is, obviously, a pretty rough assessment of proportion.

Secondly, large purchases such as the computers themselves are a significant expense and are usually offset against tax over a period of several years. Such purchases are referred to as 'capital expenses'. This is ostensibly to reflect the fact that the computer retains a second hand value that goes down over time. The fall in value is called depreciation, and the tax allowance for each year is meant to reflect that depreciation.

However, the treasury has recently been allowing the entire cost of computer purchases to be put against a single tax year to encourage IT investment by businesses.

Again, it is wise to discuss the implications with your accountant, as the timing of a large purchase can have tax implications (ie: you could save money by purchasing certain items before or after the end of a certain tax year).

Insurance

Medical indemnity insurance, insurance of business items against loss or damage, and (if you are an employer) employer's liability insurance, are all justifiable expenses.

Vehicle insurance is more complex, and is dealt with under vehicle expenses.

Salaries

If you employ anyone to perform some duties for your business (for example, secretarial work), then you can claim their salary and legitimate expenses towards tax. This includes work done by a spouse.

See the section on 'Employing Other People' for more information.

Study costs

This can include such items as journal subscriptions, medical and business-related books, and course fees.

Remember that business expense have to be for something that furthers your business interest (ie: you spend money to help you make more money). So, if you have to take part in appraisal to maintain your place on the performers list, then any expenses that go towards that appraisal (for example, journal subscriptions and other continuing medical education) should be a legitimate expense.

Also, if you go on a course, then the travel and subsistence costs of that course should also be a justified expense.

Again, discuss these expenses with your accountant.

Vehicle Expenses

These can be particularly difficult to calculate. You need to know the following:

- The mileage of your vehicle(s) at the start and end of the tax year.

- The proportion of your mileage that is business related for each vehicle – you can keep a full mileage log for the entire tax year, or for a representative period of the tax year (ie: an average month in the year).

- The cost of any repairs, servicing etc. carried out during that tax year.

- The cost of the fuel that you purchased during the tax year.

- The cost of your vehicle insurance for that year.

You can then use this to calculate the total cost of the vehicle(s) for the year. The real cost of the vehicle also involves depreciation. Although the real depreciation of a vehicle (how much value it has lost during the year) varies greatly by make, model, and age, for tax purposes the depreciation is handled as for any 'capital expense'.

Large purchases (such as vehicles and computers) are considered capital expenses and have a 'write down' amount for depreciation each year (for example 25% of the value per year). This means that you can put 25% of the purchase value of this item towards tax each year. If you sell any items during the tax year, then the true value of the sale is used to adjust the write down value.

The calculations are out with the scope of this book, and you should consult a medical accountant for advice on the tax effects of large purchases.

Tip:

Employed locums, or self-employed locums with an annual turnover under the VAT threshold (£60,000 in 2005), can use the simpler 'pence per mile' allowance instead if they wish.

Look up the rate for your size of car[*], and multiply your total business mileage by this rate (the rate will vary if you do more than a certain number of miles per year). This is the amount that you can claim as a vehicle expense.

---

[*] http://www.hmrc.gov.uk/rates/mileage.htm

Pension contributions

NHS Pension contributions are tax deductible[*].

Private pensions are a complex area, so you should discuss with your accountant what deductions are available.

Mobile phone costs

Unless you have a separate mobile phone purely for business calls, then you will need to make some kind of estimate of what percentage of your costs are business related. You can then multiply your total annual costs by this percentage and claim that as a legitimate expense.

Accommodation and subsistence

When away from home on business or study, then all of the costs of the accommodation and subsistence (for example, food and drink) are legitimate expenses. It is particularly important to keep receipts for subsistence, as these purchases are particularly prone to the 'what was that for?' effect come the end of the tax year.

Public transport costs

Again, these costs are legitimate expenses when travelling to and from business/study. Often these are paid in cash, so keep your tickets/receipts and don't forget about them when you are preparing your accounts.

---

[*] See Chapter 9: Pensions

Common non-allowable tax deductions

Income protection

Although this insurance is designed to protect your income, it is not a justified business expense. Because the insurance does not help your business to make more profit, it is classed as a personal expense.

Clothing

Even if you have separate clothes that you purely use for work, it is pretty unlikely that you will be able to claim this as a legitimate tax deduction.

Exceptions would be actual work uniforms, such as white coats, BASICS squad suits, safety boots for use at RTAs etc..

You should discuss any such deductions with your accountant to make sure that they are suitable.

> **Tip:**
>
> You can use the Income and Tax Calculator on the locum123.com website to estimate your annual expenses, but I strongly recommend that you consult with a specialised medical accountant.

Chapter 8:
Insurance

Medical Indemnity

As with any GP, locums GPs need full medical indemnity insurance. The various companies that provide indemnity charge different rates, and have different approaches to variations in income and workload.

For example, your rate can vary depending on the amount you earn or the number of sessions you work. If you frequently take long periods of time off (over 1 month) you may be able to get a rebate on your membership for those months.

Before deciding on an insurer, check:

- The annual fee.

- What is the shortest period of non-clinical practice that they will suspend your cover for (1 month, 3 months, not at all)? This is important if you take a few weeks off at a time and want to avoid paying for cover during these periods.

- Is there a 'run-in' period before you can access features such as suspending your membership (for example, they may not allow you to suspend your membership in the first year)?

- How do they calculate rates for part-time work?

- Non-financial considerations, such as reputation, level of cover and so on.

Vehicle Insurance

You need to make sure that your vehicle is insured for business use. Most insurers will include this cover for free, or for a low surcharge. Normal social, domestic and pleasure insurance will not cover locum GPs.

> *Caution*:
>
> Your vehicle must be insured for business use even if you don't do any home visits, because your travel from your home to the practice is classed as business use if you are self-employed. I have heard of one case where a GP with a social, domestic and pleasure insurance policy who crashed his car on the way to a home visit. Not only did the insurance company refuse to pay out, but the police prosecuted the GP for driving without insurance.

Income protection

If you are self-employed, then you won't receive income if you are ill or become unable to continue to work (other than basic state income support). So it's essential to make sure that you have excellent income protection cover.

Speak to an independent financial advisor for advice based on your own financial circumstances. You should shop around and speak to more than one advisor. Keep going round them until you get the lowest price, as most will sequentially reduce their initial commission to secure your business.

Policies are available that 'kick in' immediately when you are unable to work, but these are pretty expensive. It is more sensible to keep the equivalent of three months income in a savings account and take out income protection for any period of illness greater than this.

Note for ex-principals:

Income protection as a locum is different from most of the 'locum insurance' polices used by principals to pay for locum cover if they are ill for a prolonged period. Such polices are unlikely to cover your loss of income as a locum doctor, and ex-principals with cover already in place should discuss this with their insurance company.

Business insurance

You should check with your household insurance company regarding your business equipment (computers, doctors bag etc..). Check that they are happy to cover these items, and categorise items that you take with you for locum work as 'all risks'. Ask if you need to keep receipts for these items.

You may need to shop around – for example BMA insurance services are use to dealing with GPs, but may not offer the best rates.

Note:

Bear in mind that your home address will now also be your business address (unless you have access to an office elsewhere) - this may affect your insurance.

Life insurance

There is no difference between life insurance for a locum and for any other GP, but while you are organising your income protection, it's worth making sure that your life insurance policy is up to date. Your income will have increased from when you were an SHO, and it is wise to make sure that your policy level reflects the loss of income to your family should anything happen to you.

Chapter 9:
Pensions

NHS Pension Scheme

The NHS pension scheme gets a good name, and is widely regarded as being very good value for money.

The advantage of the NHS pension scheme is that the pension is worth 20% of gross income. You pay a 6% contribution (tax deductible, so it's closer to 3% in reality), and the government pays the other 14%.

The disadvantage of the NHS pension scheme is one that it shares with all public sector pension schemes – it is funded directly from taxation and is becoming increasingly expensive to fund. Basically, the money from current contributors to the scheme (current employees) is paying the benefits of the currently retired GPs. This differs from an investment scheme in which your contributions are invested and pay directly for your benefits when you retire. The problem is that the population is ageing rapidly, and the proportion of working doctors to retired doctors is set to fall significantly. The shortfall this creates needs to be made up from taxation, which means that current pensions may not be sustainable.

This problem has recently resulted in proposed changes to the NHS Pension scheme (2005), mainly involving proposals to raise the retirement age for new and younger members of the scheme from 60 years to 65 years. Also, with the new GMS GP contract, rules about who pays the employer's pension contributions are set to change too, so watch this space.

Superannuation of hospital locum work

Locum hospital doctors can have their income included in the NHS pension scheme (superannuation) when they work directly for NHS trusts.

Superannuation of GMS/PMS GP locum work

From 1st April 2003 (backdated to 5th April 2002), Locum GPs have been able to make contributions to the NHS pension scheme for NHS locum GP work, but the situation is a little complicated.

For GMS or PMS locum GP work, you will be able to pay NHS Pension Scheme contributions on 90% of the gross pay you receive (you have to subtract a figure of 10% from your gross income as 'expenses' for the purposes of calculation your pension contributions). You can then claim these contributions against tax.

In order to pension your income, you need to apply to your host PCT (the one that has you on their Performers List) and ask them for Forms A and B For each practice you need to record your sessions and pensionable income onto a separate Form A. The practice will countersign this form. At the end of each month you then fill in Form B (which is a sort of summary form of all the practices you have worked for over the month) and send it off with a cheque for your pension contribution.

> *Note:*
>
> Copies of forms A and B are available in Appendix C at the back of this book.

Superannuation of Out of Hours GP locum work

As of March 2005, Out of Hours GP locum work for certain out of hours providers (OOHPs) will also be open to the superannuation scheme.

If you provide locum cover for an OOH provider (OOHP) that is an NHS Pension Scheme Employing Authority, you will be able to pay NHS Pension Scheme contributions on 90% of the gross pay you receive (you have to subtract a figure of 10% from your gross income as 'expenses' for the purposes of calculating your pension contributions). You can then claim these contributions against tax.

If you are providing locum cover for an absent OOH GP, then you use Forms C and D to submit your pension claims to your host PCT (as for GMS/PMS locum work above). For regular OOH work you use the new SOLO form instead.

It's all a bit complicated, and, at the time of going to print, the pensions agency website[*] still did not have copies of the new forms available for download.

Superannuation of agency locum work

Agency locum work (or locum work carried out through your own limited company) is not eligible for NHS superannuation because you are acting as an employee of the locum agency (or your own

---

[*] http://www.nhspa.gov.uk/nhsgplocums.cfm

company in the case of limited companies). Also, you can't include private work.

Superannuation of private work

Private (non-NHS) work is not eligible for NHS superannuation.

Death in membership benefits loophole

One point to bear in mind is that there is a loophole in the death in membership benefits for your dependents, should you die or need to retire early on ill-health grounds. You need to be actually contracted and working as an NHS locum at the time of death to qualify. So should you have the misfortune to die between contracts (which, if you are working various short term bookings, will be most of the time) your dependents won't receive a penny.

Superannuation forms

Copies of the pension forms are included in Appendix C at the end of this book.

Private pensions

If you are doing a lot of locum agency work, or plan to work through a limited company, then you are strongly advised to look at private pension arrangements to replace or supplement your NHS pension. This is outside the scope of this book, so you should seek independent financial advice on your pension.

Chapter 10:
Negotiation

Introduction to negotiation

Negotiation is an area that many new locums find difficult. Negotiation is not part of medical or GP training, and few new locums have formal experience in this area.

Yet good negotiation skills are not only vital if you are to succeed in business (and locum GP work is a business), but they are also useful in many other aspects of life, from negotiating a bed time with your children, to negotiating with your friends over which film to go and see at the cinema or which restaurant to eat at.

In fact, we are all experienced negotiators, we may just not be aware of it yet. This chapter is a taster of the kinds of negotiations that will occur as a locum GP, along with some useful tips and tricks that should make those negotiations as painless and successful as possible.

What is negotiation?

Negotiation involves two parties, who each have something that the other wants, bargaining to come to an agreement that is acceptable to them both. In the case of locum work, the practice wants locum cover and the locum wants financial remuneration.

Negotiation should not be seen as adversarial, nor should it be seen as having a winner and a loser. The purpose is to find a solution in which both parties get what they want and are satisfied with the result.

The steps involved generally are:

1. Each party decides on their ideal outcome, and on the minimum outcome that they will find acceptable.

2. The parties negotiate until either their positions meet, or they have both reached their 'minimum acceptable' position without agreement.

3. If agreement is reached, then the terms of the agreement are formalised, usually in writing.

How does locum negotiation work in practice?

We can see that with respect to locum work, this means that:

*   The locum doctor decides what rates, terms and conditions s/he would consider ideal. The locum also should have some idea of the minimum rate of pay they will accept, and what are the worst terms and conditions that they will agree to.

*   The unit booking cover will also have at least some idea of what they would like to pay for locum cover, and what is the most that they are willing to pay for locum cover. They should also have considered what kind of work they would like the locum doctor to do.

- When the locum contacts a unit to offer their services, they set out the rates and terms that are their ideal, and the practice can either accept these, or propose rates and terms closer to their ideal.

- The locum either accepts these terms/rates, or proposes a compromise rate and terms of their own, and so on.

- If an agreement is reached then a verbal (or written) contract is formed for locum cover.

Conflict in negotiations

Conflicts occur frequently during negotiations. For example, a practice is looking for a locum to do home visits, but the locum they are negotiating with has a policy of not doing visits. Or a PCO wishes to pay the locum at the end of the following month to conform with their payroll procedures, but the locum has a policy of being paid within seven days of the completion of work.

Handling conflicts

The idea is to either resolve the conflict, or at least to minimise the impact of the conflict. There are essentially five ways to handle conflict:

Avoidance

This is the 'head in the sand' approach to a problem. Not useful for major issues, but ignoring small issues to concentrate on the important points can have its uses.

Collaboration

This is also referred to as 'the third way' or 'win win' negotiation. It is labour intensive, but can bring long term benefits by working out a solution that benefits both parties.

> ### *Example:*
>
> Lorna Locum is negotiating to provide long-term maternity locum cover for the Uptown Practice. The practice needs the locum to do one or two visits each day at lunchtime, but Lorna really does not want to do any visits.
>
> At first this conflict appears to make a deal impossible. However, Lorna digs a bit deeper and finds that the practice also provides a warfarin service. By agreeing to cover the daily warfarin results instead, Lorna can free up one of the other doctors to do the extra visits each day.

Competition

This approach is surprisingly common, both on the part of practices who have a 'set rate' for locums and refuse to even enter into negotiations, and on the part of locums who have a 'take it or leave it' approach to bookings.

Practices with this approach are often simply unfamiliar with having to negotiate, and some even have a negative view of anyone who suggests negotiation (perhaps their only experience of negotiation is buying a second hand car).

Also, while it is easy to see why a 'my way or the highway' approach is popular with locums in a climate of severe locum shortages, it should be born in mind that over time this 'win lose' approach usually results in the 'losers' becoming more organised and developing ways to avoid losing.

Accommodation

Basically, this style of negotiation is just giving in to the other side's demands. This is a common style for locums who are afraid of negotiation, or inexperienced.

It used to be a common style when locum work was hard to find (and complements the other side taking a competitive approach as described above).

It can be a useful tactic if you suddenly find that you have made a mistake and are keen to minimise the damage caused.

Example:

Lorna Locum has accidentally double booked a practice, causing terrible problems for them when she has to cancel at only a few hours notice.

The practice manager later contacts Lorna as the practice are now looking for cover on an alternative date later in the week. Lorna had been planning to go out shopping with her sister on that afternoon, but to rescue her good name agrees to the practice manager's request.

Compromise

This is perhaps the best-known negotiation technique. Basically the two parties meet somewhere in the middle. It can involve several bids from each side, each one moving closer to the middle until the bids either meet (and a deal is reached), or people stop bidding (when a deal is not reached).

The Win-Lose Matrix

When we put the above techniques together, we form the Win-Lose Matrix.

Win-Lose Matrix

	Locum Wins	**Locum Loses**
Practice Wins	Collaboration	Accommodation
Practice Loses	Competition	Avoidance

Note: Compromise falls into the middle of the table (win/lose for both the locum and the practice).

Must I negotiate?

Well, yes and no. Due to the current market, in which there is a significant shortage of locum doctors, complex negotiation is usually not required. The locum doctor sets out their rates/terms and the practice either accepts them, or has to try and find another locum. However, this is simply competition negotiation as described above and has its drawbacks.

Or, you can simply accept the rate that the practice offers and leave everything up to them. This avoids any active negotiation, but is also just another style of negotiation (accommodation, as seen above).

So you can't really avoid negotiation because it's an integral part of booking locum work, but in most cases you don't need to enter into complex negotiations.

Know what you want

Before you can negotiate effectively, you need to know what it is that you want from the negotiations. Often this is as simple as 'how much do I want to get paid', but of course terms and conditions like 'I don't want to do any home visits' come into this too.

Spend some time looking at the sections of this book that deal with setting your locum rates and terms and conditions first. Then you should list, if only mentally, the order of importance of your various terms. Set a range of rates that you would be happy with, so that you can aim for your top rate, still have room for negotiation if the need arises, but will know what your minimum acceptable rate will be.

Do your research

The more you know about the practice you are negotiating with, and about the market conditions of the area you are planning to work in, the better your negotiations will be.

Find out what rates other locums in the area charge, and roughly what terms you can expect to obtain. Compare this to rates and terms for work nearby (or further away if you are willing to travel).

Are there any special considerations – for example, is there a conference on that lots of the local GPs are wanting to go to which will make finding locum cover more difficult for the practices in the area?

Value added services

The more you can offer a practice, the stronger your position. Even in a market where there is a shortage of locums, and you could find work by simply falling out of bed, it still pays to have an edge on other locums that will make practices more keen to book you. The more offers of work you have, the stronger your negotiating position.

For example, you may be especially skilled at helping practices hit their quality targets which will give them a strong financial incentive to book you, even if you cost a bit more than other locums in the area.

Avoiding unfair negotiation tricks

Some practices will use tricks or strategies to try and inhibit your negotiation and get a better deal for themselves.

These strategies can include:

The 'You're the only one who charges these rates' gambit

This may, or may not, be true. It's largely irrelevant, as if they can get the work done more cheaply elsewhere, then they are free to do so. However, it's best to bypass this approach and try to focus on the main negotiation.

The 'We have a set rate' gambit

Units can decide whether to enforce such a policy or not, so this is of no relevance to you. Ignore this tack, and direct the negotiation back to the main points (rates and terms). You can also try pointing out that you can't let practices set rates as this would undermine your tax position (and could result in the tax man asking them for pension and NI contributions from them at a later date).

The 'We only get a set re-imbursement for locum cover' gambit

This can be a genuine problem, because lack of funds can prevent successful negotiation. However, it is always important to verify such statements and not just take them at face value. Politely request the details of the person who sets the re-imbursement level so that you can verify this. If they decline, then you have to assume that they are not being entirely truthful.

The 'Big chair, little chair' gambit

In face to face negotiations, watch out for physical attempts to undermine you. Very hot rooms, uncomfortable small chairs for you with nice big comfy chairs for them, deliberate height disadvantage. If this occurs, point out gently that this is making you uncomfortable and ask for a change in venue.

The 'You won't get a partnership with this attitude' gambit

One sees less of this tactic just now, as partnerships are currently less popular than they used to be. If you encounter this approach, which demonstrates a significant degree of arrogance on the part of the negotiator, you should ignore it and concentrate on the real negotiation points. Of course, this tactic is often a sign of deeper problems, and it is often best to avoid such units if possible.

What if a unit won't negotiate?

You will come across situations where practices will stick stubbornly to their ideal position, and will just not be willing to negotiate. This can be quire frustrating, especially if their position is just beyond your minimum acceptable position. However, there is nothing you can do about this other than to gently, politely, but firmly, walk away from the negotiation. You can leave the door open for them to return if they change their minds.

Using provisional bookings

Sometimes it is useful to provisionally hold dates for a unit to give them time to decide if they want to accept your terms or not. This can be helpful in concentrating their attention, and gives a deadline after which you are free to book cover elsewhere.

You should be careful to make it clear to the practice when the provisional booking expires, and what they need to do to convert this to a confirmed booking before this time.

Offering escape routes

It can also be useful to provide an escape route for them to 'save face' if they do change their minds. For example, if a practice say that they have a 'set locum rate' and that it is non negotiable, you could explain that you are required to set your own rates and terms as part of your self employment status, and to do otherwise could compromise your tax status.

Closing the deal

Once you feel that you have reached an acceptable agreement, close by summarising the deal you have reached.

This avoids misunderstandings, and can simply be done verbally. However, it is a very good idea to use a written quote and terms document* which you can send to the practice. Ideally the practice

---

* See the template document in Appendix C at the back of this book.

should sign and return the document to indicate that they understand the deal and are in agreement.

Summary

So we have seen in this chapter that negotiation is not as tough as it looks – it's simply an extension into business of skills that all of us use on a daily basis.

With knowledge of the types of negotiation, some of the techniques that you can use to improve negotiations, and some of the negative approaches that practices might use, you should be able to negotiate better rates and terms with practices, while at the same time providing a better service for them and their patients.

Chapter 11:
Practicalities of Locum Work

Qualifications, Performer Lists and other requirements

UK Requirements for locum doctors

To work as a locum doctor in the UK you need:

- To be eligible for registration with the General Medical Council (GMC)
- Usually you will require 2-3 referees
- Hold a current Hep B vaccination certificate

To work as a locum GP you must also have:

- A certificate of satisfactory completion of GP Vocational Training from the Joint Committee on Postgraduate Training (JCPTGP) or a Certificate of Completion of

Training (CCT) from the Postgraduate Medical Education and Training Board (PMETB)[*].

- Inclusion on a relevant Performers List – this is a list held by PCTs and Health Boards of all GPs registered in their area.

- A drivers' licence valid in the UK (if you intend to do home visits).

Vocational Training

Vocational Training became mandatory for GP principals in 1981, and for all doctors working in General Practice (except registrars) in 1995.

> **Note:**
>
> A Certificate of Satisfactory Completion of Vocational GP Training from another EU country is considered as equivalent to a UK Vocational Training certificate. Contact the Postgraduate Medical Education and Training Board (PMETB) for more advice on this[†].

For more information, see the JCPTGP's booklet ' Guide To Certification'.

---

[*] On the 30th of September 2005, the Joint Committee on Postgraduate Training (JCPTGP) was merged with the Specialist Training Authority to form the Postgraduate Medical Education and Training Board (PMETB).

[†] Postgraduate Medical Education and Training Board (PMETB) website:

http://www.pmetb.org.uk

Exemption from Vocational Training

You are exempt from the Vocational Training requirement if you were practicing as a GP principal before 15th February 1981.

However, GPs practicing before 15th of February 1981 are only exempt from the Vocational Training requirements if they joined a Health Authority list by the 15th of February 1990. So GPs who practiced in the UK before 1981, and have since been working abroad, will not be able to claim the exemption if they return to the UK.

GP Performers Lists

Inclusion on a single English Performers List allows you to practice anywhere in England. The same is true for the Welsh Performers Lists. However, in Scotland you need to be included in the Performers List of each PCT/Health Board where you want to work. When you apply for your first (or 'home') Scottish Performers List, you will be asked if you want to be included in any other PCT/Health Board lists as well. It's best to select every PCT/Health Board to avoid delays should you wish to work elsewhere at a later date.

The Performers Lists replace the Supplementary Lists of locum GPs. If you were on a Supplementary List, you should have automatically been transferred to the Performers List in April 2004.

Caution:

The application procedure now includes a full Criminal Background Check, which can take up to six weeks, so apply early for each country in the UK to avoid problems later (see advice to registrars, below).

GP Registrars coming to the end of their training

Delays in obtaining your Certificate of Completion of Training (CCT) at the end of GP training are a frequent cause of complaint amongst newly qualified GPs. You cannot work as a locum GP until you have this certificate in your possession, so it's vital to make sure that you get your paperwork off to the Postgraduate Medical Education and Training Board (PMETB) as early as possible.

Warning:

You should not delay your application to be placed on the performers list by waiting until you have your Certificate of Completion of Training(CCT), because the application can take up to six weeks to process.

You should apply for inclusion on the Performers Lists (see section above) as early as possible (at least 2 months before you complete your VTS training).

They will process the time consuming parts of your application, and you can then submit your Certificate of Completion of Training when it arrives.

Once your referees and Criminal Background Check have been processed, a PCO should be able to complete the rest of an urgent application within one to two working days.

The Joint Committee on Postgraduate Training (JCPTGP) says "A VTR form can be signed and submitted to the JCPTGP four weeks before the final day of training in that post but no earlier than this...You do not have to wait until the end of your training before asking the Committee to assess your experience. The Joint Committee strongly recommends that all but the final VTR form be submitted to the Committee as early as possible so that the majority of the applicant's documentation can be checked in advance of the applicant making a formal application for a certificate. This will avoid delays in the issuing of the certificate."[*]

---

[*] At the time of going to press the Postgraduate Medical Education and Training Board (PMETB) which replaced the Joint Committee on the 30th of September 2005 had not yet issued guidance to replace this.

You should check the PMETB website for details of any changes in their procedures.

http://www.pmetb.org.uk

Professional development and re-accreditation

There are several aspects of professional development and re-accreditation which present unique problems for locum GPs.

Prescribing patterns

Until locum GPs are able to have their own prescribing numbers, it's almost impossible for a locum to monitor their prescribing patterns.

The only time that prescribing can be monitored is when providing vacancy cover for a single-handed practice for several months. It is my experience that locum GPs actually have a low prescribing pattern compared with principals (around 20% lower). The reasons for this are unknown. It is possible it is due to lower chronic disease prescribing, as the locum may delay costly treatment options until the new principal arrives.

Personal prescribing numbers for locum GPs are in the pipeline.

Referral patterns

Another difficulty is monitoring the number and quality of locum referrals.

This is, however, easier than prescribing patterns without a personal number. You can keep track of your referral patterns by recording all of your referrals and then auditing them at a later date.

There is a Dictation List form at the end of this book. This can be used to store referral data which can be followed up later. It is possible to either wait until you are in the same practice and ask to see the notes of patients to follow up what happened to your referral, or to write to a practice at a later date asking for copies of the relevant letters.

> *Caution:*
>
> Locums must be sensitive to Data Protection issues here. Patient data must be stored securely, and when asking for documents to be sent by post it is essential that the delivery address is secure.

Re-accreditation

The programme for locum re-accreditation is still being developed at the time of writing. The same issues than make professional development difficult for locums, mean that there are practical problems with the implementation of re-accreditation for locum GPs.

Annual appraisal

You should contact your host PCO regarding the setup and funding of your annual appraisal.

Some PCOs have been trying to avoid funding locums' appraisals, but the money for this was negotiated and provided for in their budgets. If you have problems with funding or provision of appraisal from your PCO, speak to the BMA or ask for advice on the doctors.net.uk GP non-principal discussion forum[*].

---

[*] http://www.doctors.net.uk

Equipment and drugs

Medical items

What medical equipment you take with you depends on the kind of locum work is involved, how long you are going for, personal preference and the transport arrangements.

I take much more equipment when I go by car to a remote locum to do on call than I do when going by train or plane to a clinic based locum with no on call. I find using someone else's equipment is quite a hassle, so generally speaking the more personal medical equipment you can take with you the easier your locums will be.

There is a list of suggestions for locum GP items in Appendix D at the end of this book.

Out of hours drugs

You can obtain drugs for use in locum work in one of three ways:

1. Issue a private prescription to yourself (you can print it out or handwrite it on any blank paper). You can find that iv drugs are hard to get in small quantities because the pharmacy will need to order an entire box of each item, but shop around. Remember, this is a legitimate business expense, so you will get up to 40% of the cost back from tax.

2. Ask a tame practice if they would be willing to donate a few of their cheaper stock order drugs to a worthy cause (I'm not sure of the legality of this option from an NHS point of view, but assuming you use these drugs on NHS patients, I can't see any problems with the morality of it).

3. Accumulate 'free' samples from drug reps. This is the cheapest option (for the locum, anyway, as often these are 'loss leaders' of expensive drugs), but personally I think if

you are going to charge professional rates, then you should provide a professional service.

Tip:

Request practices replace any drugs that you use, as this can be achieved quite simply via their stock order forms.

Some suggestions for out of hours drugs are listed in Appendix D at the end of this book.

Controlled Drugs

These can be obtained in the same manner as the drugs above (except, that you won't get these free from drug reps!).

When ordering from a pharmacist, the prescription is called a 'requisition' and it is best to handwrite it on paper with your letterhead on it (the letterhead should include your professional title and capacity). Include the total quantity required in numbers and words and the intended purpose (eg: 'to be used for patients in capacity as locum GP').

Caution:

Controlled drugs must be kept in a locked box which itself should be in a locked box. A small cash box stored in a locked boot is ideal. If you have an estate car (the interior of a car is not considered a locked box, but the boot of a car is), then store the cash box in a locking glove box or car safe.

---

116 Locum Doctor Survival Guide

The Misuse of Drugs Act (1971) and the Misuse of Drugs Regulations (1985) require a controlled drug register be kept. This should be a sealed book (not loose leaf) with numbered pages, recording dates, amounts, purchases, and administration.

You should record supplies as:

- Date supply received

- The name and address of supplier

- Amount obtained

- Running total in stock (optional, but recommended)

You should record use as:

- Date given

- The name and address of patient

- Amount given

- Running total in stock (optional, but recommended)

You should make the entries in chronological order, and you can make corrections as additional notes, but you may not score out or delete any entries.

Drug expiry dates

One of the main problems for GP with out of hours/emergency drugs is that they tend to go out of date just before you need to use them.

You can simply go through your bag each month and check the dates by hand, replacing the ones that are near expiry, but this is time consuming.

Keeping a database of your drugs

Another option is to keep a database or spreadsheet of the drugs on a PDA or computer. You can then sort the list by expiry date and check it each month for drugs that are near to replacement.

There are various programs available for the different computer platforms that are suitable – Microsoft Excel being one of the best known ones.

What to record in your drug database:

- Drug name

- Formulation (tabs, injection, etc..)

- Dose

- Number held

- Manufacturer

- Lot number

- Expiry date

Simplifying re-ordering

Recording the details this way makes it easy to order replacement drugs, as you can simply cut and paste the details into a word document to print out a prescription request. If you format the page correctly, you can print such a document directly onto a stock order form.

Tip:

To get the sort function in your database or spreadsheet to work, you need to format the date correctly. Make sure that the column that you use is set to 'date' format, and not just plain text. Alternatively, simply write the date with the year first (eg: 2008.10) which will sort properly using an alphabetical list.

Personal items

There are also quite a few personal items that can make residential locum work much easier. For example a laptop computer that plays DVDs, and a portable printer.

I keep most of these items in a large "gadget" bag than can be easily carried. Don't forget to insure these items as 'all risks' with your household insurer.

There is a list of suggested items in Appendix D at the end of this book.

Working away from home

How can I keep in touch when I am on the move?

Keeping in touch on the move includes mobile solutions for receiving mail, phone calls, email, faxes and having internet access. Keeping in touch with your financial situation is also important.

> ### *Tip*:
>
> *If* you are working away from home then you need to try and do as much of your own paperwork when you are away as possible - otherwise you will come home for a few days off and spend all of them answering final demands for bill payments etc..

Mail forwarding

Mail forwarding is important if you are going to be away for more than a couple of weeks at a time. If someone is at home they can either deal with your mail themselves or forward or fax it to you, but the solution I use is Mail Boxes Etc.[*] They will give you a post box address for your letters and sign for any parcels that arrive. You can pick up your post from your box 24 hours a day and they can forward the post and parcels to you wherever you are. They can also provide office solutions such as photocopying, printing, laminating and binding so you can have your own office staff for a

---

[*] http://www.mbe.uk.com

fraction of the normal cost. One other advantage is that you can give out your postal address freely without giving out your physical home address.

> *Tip*:
>
> You need to be careful about giving out your address - I've even had one patient turn up at the Mail Boxes office to pay a private fee in cash (which the staff put in my mail box with an explanatory note).

Mobile phone

A mobile phone is pretty much mandatory for a locum. It is obviously best to use a company with good coverage in the areas you are going to work. A dual band (or tri-band if you go to the US or Canada to work or for a holiday) phone is useful as this will allow you to make emergency calls on any network.

> *Tip:*
>
> If you don't want to be disturbed on your days off, but don't want to miss important messages, some modern phones (for example, the Sony Ericsson P910i) can screen calls for you. I have mine set up to recognise my friends and family, but to automatically divert other callers to my voicemail.

Voicemail

It is now possible to receive your voicemail messages as SMS text messages via a company called Spinvox[*]. This is very handy for locum work, as you may receive a large number of voicemails regarding locum work and receiving them as SMS text messages is far easier.

Email

Email on the move is very useful and can be achieved by one of several methods.

- Take a laptop or palmtop computer and connect to the internet via a landline or mobile phone. If you buy a mobile phone with an infrared or Bluetooth® built-in modem, then you don't need any extra cables to connect via you mobile phone.

- Some modern mobile phones allow you to send and receive email via the phone.

- Set up an internet-based email account and pick up your messages from any internet-connected computer (eg: at the practices where you are working). Doctors.net.uk[†] is the most useful of these services for locums because they are the only internet-based email service that is cleared for use via nhs.net.

Faxes

A useful thing for locum work is a fax mailbox. You are given a fax number for people to send faxes to, and when you receive a fax you are notified by email or SMS text message. You can then receive

---

[*] http://www.spinvox.com

[†] http://www.doctors.net.uk

your fax as an email attachment, and send faxes by email. eFax[*] are the most well known provider of this service.

Internet Access

Most practices have internet access in their consulting rooms, but a laptop computer is very useful when locuming away from home.

Banking

You can take care of your finances by online banking. First Direct[†] offer free internet and mobile phone banking. They will send mini-statements as SMS messages to your phone, and text messages when your account reaches a certain limit or transactions over a certain amount occur.

Will I want to take a partner/children/pets with me if I travel?

If you are away from home for significant periods then you probably will. In General Practice and senior hospital locum work it is common for locums to take their family with them if they are going to be away from home for more than a week or two.

Negotiate before you go to have decent double/family accommodation provided. Not everyone agrees on this, but I am of the opinion that the practice/hospital/trust should pay for all of this for you. Some practices feel that doing a residential locum is a "busman's holiday" and expect you to pay for your family if you bring them. This may be true if you do two weeks a year of residential work and spend the rest of the time at home, but if the majority of your work is residential then you will end up paying thousands of pounds a year for the privilege of being away from home and dragging you partner or family around the country.

---

[*] http://www.efax.com

[†] http://www.firstdirect.com

> *Note:*
>
> Think of what you have at home, that you will miss when you are away - your satellite widescreen TV, power shower, comfy leather sofa, exercise bike etc..
>
> This is why most doctors do not want to do much residential locum work - so if the accommodation does not reflect this then your rates should.

If the practice or trust are not paying for accommodation then you will need to recoup these costs through your earnings and your rates should reflect this as well.

Consider how will your family get about and what will they do while you are working. This may entail taking a second car with you or renting one when you are there.

Some locums take their pets with them - dogs and cats are most common, but I've even seen one locum with his parrot! It is advisable to inform the practice/trust of this before you arrive in case there are accommodation exclusions.

Miscellaneous

Obtaining a mortgage when you are self-employed

You should be aware that becoming self-employed can significantly affect your credit rating.

Most lenders will want to see two to three years accounts before they will provide a mortgage or other loan. In fact, I discovered to my horror when I first became a locum GP that I was even unable to rent a TV without two years accounts.

The best way to avoid problems is, quite simply, to avoid needing to borrow money in your first two years as a locum – either get your mortgage before you stop being employed, or wait until you have two years accounts.

However, there are other ways around this problem:

- Some lenders will accept a letter from your accountant stating what your projected income is likely to be.

- Some lenders have more experience with GPs than others – GPs have a better safety record for lending than most self-employed people.

- Some lenders have 'Professional' mortgages aimed specifically at GPs, Lawyers and other professionals.

- You can investigate a 'self-certificate' mortgage, which may not require you to produce accounts.

Chapter 12:
Clinical Aspects of Locum Work

Continuity of Care

Loss of continuity

The first key difference you will notice when you start working as a locum is the loss of continuity of care. Like oxygen, continuity is one of those things that you really don't take much notice of until you don't have any. In long term locum cover, or regular sessions, continuity is not as big an issue. But for many locums providing short term sessions across numerous practices, or even across a large geographical area, the loss of continuity can be quite disconcerting.

Advantages of discontinuity

Having said that, there are some advantages to not having continuity. The first is that 'heartsink' patients don't seem nearly so bad when you know you are not going to have to see them again! The second, more useful, aspect is that you can approach patients with fresh eyes. Often familiarity can breed not so much contempt as complacency. If you try doing a google groups search for 'locum doctor' you will find numerous examples of patients who were delighted to see a locum doctor because they were "finally taken seriously". On the other hand, patients with chronic fatigue syndrome and other controversial diagnoses seem to have a particular dislike of locums. Whether this is because they value continuity more than most, or that locums view the fact that they will never have to see the patient again as an opportunity to 'tell it like it is', is unclear.

Lack of follow up

The greatest danger from the loss of continuity is that there is no chance to correct any errors. Locums have to rely on the next doctor to pick up where they left off, sometimes without any clear idea of who that next doctor will be. It is therefore even more important to have clear, legible, notes which leave a clear indication of not only what has been done already, but what the plan for follow up is.

Mistakes that happen after you leave

Also, locums are very vulnerable to practice mistakes happening after the locum has gone on their merry way (for example, losing a dictation tape). The first thing the locum may know about it is when they get the letter of complaint.

Anecdote:

I once phoned up a consultant, to check if he had been happy with the locum cover I had provided as a locum medical RMO, only to be asked what I had been playing at as I had missed the diabetic ketoacidosis the night before which had resulted in the death of a patient. This was the first I had heard of the patient, as I had had an undisturbed night's sleep. It turned out that the House Officer has seen the patient during the night but had not thought it necessary to contact me, and had not mentioned it to me in the morning.

Isolation and Education

Locum work is isolating

The professional isolation of locum work can not only be quite depressing, but can produce problems with medical education and management of difficult cases. For example, it is almost impossible to build up a traditional network of clinical support, or your own medical library in the consulting room, such as you would have if you were a principal in your own practice.

Using the internet to overcome isolation

The internet is an invaluable resource for overcoming isolation. Online medical discussion forums, and online medical textbooks and encyclopaedias, have revolutionised mobile access to medical information.

Online medical discussion forums

By using online communities of doctors, such as the forums on doctors.net.uk[*], a locum can maintain a 'virtual network' of colleagues to ask questions of and to generally moan to when things are tough.

Online medical library

Not having access to your own 'medical library' is a problem that the internet can help with too. Almost all practices have internet access in their consulting rooms, and you can use this to access online medical information and textbooks[†] such as the British

---

[*] http://www.doctors.net.uk

[†] See Appendix A at the back of this book.

National Formulary[*], the medical wikipedia GANFYD[†], and the online medical textbook eMedicine[‡].

> **Tip:**
>
> I use a .Mac[§] account to store copies of my internet bookmarks, address book, and calendar so that I can access them from an internet-connected computer.

Practice meetings

It is also important to try and be as outgoing as possible, and attend local educational and practice events whenever possible. Obviously, where these are work related you should be paid, but often practices will invite you to their lunchtime or evening educational events outside your work hours. Some practices have a poor view of locums and will not bother to invite you to such meetings (or may even actively discourage your attendance). These practices should be avoided.

---

[*] http://www.bnf.org.uk

[†] http://ganfyd.org

[‡] http://www.emedicine.com

[§] .Mac accounts are available to Apple Macintosh users for a small annual fee via the apple website http://www.apple.com

The 'buddy' system

A few switched-on practices implement a 'buddy' system for locums. Each locum is allocated a 'buddy' principal or salaried doctor who they can go to for help and advice. This is an excellent system, and I would recommend it to all practices.

Communication

Communication, communication, communication

I've often said that the biggest two problems with locum work are communication and communication. It is just very difficult to communicate properly as a locum. I have dealt with the problems of receiving post, email and faxes when 'on the road', but there are also problems with intra-practice communication and primary care-secondary care communication.

Lack of familiarity causes errors

The main problem is that, as with so many other aspects of locum cover, you are working in an unfamiliar system. So it is vital to be as organised as possible, and to have a fixed personal routine, that you can super-impose the local system onto.

It is always useful to explain to a practice with an unusual communication system that you will need special treatment to avoid messages going astray.

Having your own results stamp[*] can be useful, as it makes it clear who checked the result and when. You can now design your own results stamp, with your name and contact details on it, online[†].

---

[*] For example, a results stamp with your name and contact details on it, a date stamp, and a series of tick boxes for 'File, Normal, Notes, and Action' – it is, of course, vital to make sure that the staff in the practice understand what these tick boxes mean. I use the practice results stamp as well, if one is available.

[†] http://www.rubberstampz.co.uk

> **Tip:**
>
> You can use a dictation list* to keep track of referrals and other tasks to minimise the risk of the task being missed, especially after you have left.

Intra-practice communication

Every practice is different, and how the different members of the primary care team communicate varies enormously. At one end of the scale, some practices have GPs, nurses and clerical staff that talk to each other almost exclusively by internal email without ever leaving their rooms. At the other extreme, there are practices where all communication occurs in the coffee room. In between we have practices that use post-its, practices that use memo sheets, practices that have daily or twice-daily meetings, practices that use voicemail, practices that have bespoke IT messaging services, and so on.

> **Comment:**
>
> Of course, the worst kind of practice is the one in which communication just does not take place at all (which is sadly more common that one might imagine!). These are best avoided, as the risk of errors is greatly increased and because, frankly, they are depressing places to work.

---

* A Dictation List template is included in Appendix C at the end of this book, and is available for download as part of the Locum Survival Pack from the locum123.com website:

http://www.locum123.com/survival_pack.shtml

Primary-Secondary Care Communication

The same issues apply here too, but there is thankfully less variation on the whole. However, be on your toes for differences between units that use formal referral letters versus those that use some form of referral template (a good medical secretary will simply apply your dictation to their local style, but some secretaries can be confused when confronted by what, to them, is an unusual style of dictation).

Some units use a pre-printed form for physiotherapy and other PAMs referrals, whilst others require a dictated letter. Specialist clinics, and the types of conditions they accept, vary from location to location as well.

Not knowing the local consultants or secondary care setup can cause problems when trying to arrange urgent admissions or clinic attendances.

> *Example*:
>
> In my experience the most embarrassing example of this problem is when a patient attends who needs to be seen urgently at a GUM or STD clinic. It's not much fun (for you or the patient), when you are forced to call the front desk for advice on the next 'clap clinic' while the patient is still in the room. Few patients wish to be called later in the day with the information either!

Many practices now have a locum information pack containing information about referrals and local secondary care facilities, but the quality of these packs is sadly quite variable.

> *Tip:*
>
> The Practice Details sheet[*] can be used to record local referral policies and clinics.

Arranging Follow Up and Safety Netting

Safety netting is an even more important concept for locums than it is for permanent GPs. It is important to make sure that patients are aware of when to return for follow up, and by what point they should expect to have heard about further care such as referral appointments. Medico-legally, however, this is not enough and it is important to leave a written handover of key outstanding tasks when you leave. I use the Dictation List[*] to record these tasks, and ask the staff to sign and return these lists to me when the tasks have been completed.

Managing different styles of care

One of the most challenging aspects of locum work is having to function in a wide range of clinical styles. Different practices, and individual GPs within each practice, can have quite different styles of practice.

Most of these differences are just simply 'style', but some aspects have medico-legal and safety implications. For example,

---

[*] See Appendix C at the back of this book.

differences in attitude towards risk can cause locums who have a lower risk threshold to be uncomfortable, or even unable to function, in that practice. Differences in prescribing of certain drugs, such as benzodiazepines for insomnia, or antibiotics for viral sore throats, or prescribing over the phone for coughs and colds, or the use of homeopathic or alternative treatments, can all cause problems for locums.

Note:

Problems with style are especially acute for locums who hold strong views on certain treatments, or who have a very distinctive style themselves. I certainly found this most difficult when I first started locum work and was used to just one style of general practice. As time passed, I realised that there is no one right way to do anything in medicine (although, there are also lots of wrong ways to do things!)

Handling poor care

Encountering poor care is what every locum dreads. We all make mistakes from time to time (hopefully not too serious ones!), we are all better at some things than others, and there is always something that we will be better at than the person we are covering for (and vice versa).

However, from time to time we all encounter a poorly performing doctor. Sometimes this is a health related issue – the doctor may be depressed, or have an alcohol or drug problem. Often this is why the practice needed a locum in the first place. At other times there may be just seriously substandard care (such as dangerous prescribing, or a series of major mistakes). In rare cases there may be evidence of illegal activity, such as significant quantities of missing controlled drugs or financial fraud (although, the latter would need to be pretty blatant to be obvious to an everyday locum).

Whatever the cause, this can be a difficult and unsettling experience. Clearly, your first responsibility lies with patient safety, but you also have to consider the danger to the doctor of having an untreated health problem. Vitally, you must also protect yourself – both from allegations of failure to act to protect patients, and from any attempt on the part of the doctor or associated parties to undermine you or to retaliate against you.

There are various ways to approach this problem, and the best approach is very much dependant on the details of the individual case:

- How serious is the risk to patients?

- Who else is in place to help (partners, practice manager, practice nurse)?

- What support do you have locally?

- What support does the doctor in question have?

- How much documentary evidence do you have that the problem exists?

The best advice is to approach an independent, senior colleague that you trust and discuss with them. However, make sure that you write everything down – patient details, dates, times, concerns, conversations you have etc.. You will probably want to talk to your defence organisation for advice as well.

Caution:

If you come across evidence that a colleague has a health problem, which is a threat to patients, but you do not act to protect those patients, then you could be found guilty of Serious Professional Misconduct while the problem doctor may not (as health issues are considered a separate problem under GMC rules).

Patient Complaints

Patient complaints are a fact of life for GPs today. This does not make them any less distressing. They usually occur locally via the practice, either verbally or in writing, where they are usually handled by local resolution. However, patients can also lodge complaints with the local PCO, or even directly with the GMC.

Locum vulnerability to complaints

Sadly, locums are particularly vulnerable to complaints. This is partly because patients do not have the same long term relationship with locums, and therefore do not have 'anything to lose' by making a complaint. It is also partly because dealing with unfamiliar patients in an unfamiliar location is much more difficult and misunderstandings and errors are therefore more common.

Caution:

There is another less pleasant reason why locums are more vulnerable to complaints. Although most GP surgeries are very understanding and helpful in the case of a complaint, some units – and this includes PCOs as well as practices – have a very negative view of locums and appear quite happy to 'drop the locum in it' to protect themselves. This is particularly insidious on those occasions when the locum is not informed of the complaint, or is excluded from the complaint process.

PCO Complaints

Many PCOs now make placement on their Performers List dependent on the locum agreeing in writing to comply with their complaints process. It is worth finding out what your local procedure is.

Although one would expect PCOs to handle complaints more professionally than individual practices, this is not my experience. PCOs are often understaffed and overworked, and the quality of investigations varies significantly complaint.

Sadly, few units have a formal policy as to how locum doctors should be involved and kept informed of the progress of a complaint, so it is advisable to include conditions for this in your booking terms (see below).

Handling local complaints

Most complaints relate to communication problems or misunderstanding, both of which are intrinsically more likely when providing locum cover. Most complainants are simply looking for an explanation of what went wrong and why, and an assurance that it will not happen again in the future (either to them, or to someone else).

> *Note:*
>
> Businesses refer to the process of handling a complaint as 'recovery'. The good news is that a well handled recovery of a minor complaint actually leads to higher satisfaction levels than if a minor error had not occurred in the first place. The bad news is that nothing makes clients see red more than a badly handled complaint. Obviously, opportunities for a refund or future discount are limited in the NHS, but apologies are always free.

Whilst it is important to be open and honest about what happened, you should avoid directly admitting liability (especially if you were not at fault) and patients rarely want an in depth description of the internal workings of the practice in question. What is more important is a description of what has been learnt, and how you are going to avoid this in the future. If no error occurred, but there was simply a misunderstanding, then it is worth explaining the misunderstanding and exploring how the information will be made more clear in the future. Remember to make the reply easily understood, avoid jargon and explain jargon where it is unavoidable.

Caution:

Whilst minor local complaints can often be handled with a simply explanation and/or apology, and an attempt to set things straight, you should of course contact your medical defence union if you receive a local complaint that is either serious, vexatious, or could lead to litigation.

Including complaints handling in your terms and conditions

To help protect yourself, it is wise to have a clause in your terms and conditions regarding complaints.

It is useful to have a time limit within which a unit will provide you with a copy of the complaint and any relevant clinical notes. You should also consider requiring units to keep you fully informed of all correspondence related to the complaint process. You will want to see a copy of the response that the practice sends to the patient, preferably before it is sent.

GMC Complaints

GMC Complaints are particularly distressing. Complaints to the GMC are rising rapidly, and an increasing number of complainants are going directly to the GMC with their complaint, bypassing local resolution.

Removal from the GMC website

The GMC has a formal protocol, which it initiates when a complaint is received. Firstly, they will remove you from the online register – this has serious implications for locums, because every practice that is thinking about employing you will find that you have 'vanished' from the GMC website. Recent publicity around the problems with this policy has helped, but many practices will still have significant reservations about employing you when you have an outstanding complaint with the GMC. This means that your livelihood can be placed in serious jeopardy for a significant length of time even with relatively trivial complaints.

Interim Orders Panel

If the complaint contains serious allegations, which pose a potential threat to patient safety, then you may be subjected to an Interim Panel Order which will place conditions on your practice while the complaint is being investigated.

Employers disclosure

The GMC will write to you, enclosing a copy of the complaint, and will ask you to provide a list of recent employers (covering anything from the last 6 months to 5 years). They will then contact your employers to ask if they have any concerns about you. Again, this can cause serious problems for a locum GP, who may have dozens of employers. They will also ask you to respond to the complaint, and they will share your response with the complainant. At this stage you can make further comments before they decide whether to proceed to a Fitness to Practice hearing or not.

Fitness to Practice

If your case proceeds to Fitness to Practice, and you are found to be guilty of professional misconduct, then punishment can range from an admonishment, through conditions and temporary suspension (3 months to 3 years usually), to erasure from the register (for at least 5 years). Again, locums are more vulnerable to the fallout from such penalties because of the need to continually apply for work and because of the lack of a natural support network. For example, GP partnerships are able to support one of their partners through the process and minor penalties.

The entire process can easily take over a year, and you should of course contact your medical defence organisation as soon as you receive a complaint from the GMC.

Chapter 13:
Variety in Locum Work

Working Out of Hours

Background to Out of Hours in the UK

Up until April 2004 most OOH care had been provided in the UK by co-operatives of GPs working together. The co-op hourly pay rates had been artificially depressed by the fact that the pay was essentially circular (ie: the more GPs paid themselves to do shifts, the more they had to pay into the co-op to keep it going). This meant that night rates were significantly lower than daytime locum rates in many areas.

Recent changes to GP Out of Hours

The ability to opt out of 24 hour care is one of the cornerstones of the 2004 new GMS contract. With the PCTs taking over responsibility for OOH, there are opportunities for locums to negotiate higher rates of pay for difficult to fill shifts. OOH sessions are becoming more intensive, and less popular, than before because PCTs want to maximise the use of the GPs they employ.

> *Comment*:
>
> Nurses and paramedics are unlikely to replace OOH GPs in the short to medium term, as there are shortages of staff with appropriate experience, they have high training costs, see less patients per hour, and refer more patients to secondary care. Even a small increase in the referral rate to secondary care will far outweigh any payroll savings.

Issues to consider when arranging out of hours work

There are several issues to consider when booking OOH work:

- What is the intensity of work likely to be? How many patients are you willing to see per hour? How many visits are you willing to do per hour?

- Unsocial hours should attract a 33% to 100% higher fee than normal hours (or more, depending on demand).

- If you are going to be driven (possibly at speed using green flashing lights), what level of advanced driver training have the drivers been given?

- Will the unit accept your terms and conditions regarding the maximum number of patients that will be seen per hour?

- Will you be required to 'cover' nurses who are working in another centre? If so, are you willing to take clinical responsibility for decisions made by staff you have never met and who's training you have not been privy to?

- How long will it take to get paid? PCOs can take up to two months to pay locums via their payroll system.

Remote Areas

Introduction to remote GP work

Locum work can be very varied, and one of the most enjoyable and challenging aspects of locum work is that you can find yourself in places that you have never been before, faced with problems that you have never dealt with before.

For example, what would you do if you were the only doctor on a small island. cut off from the mainland by a fierce storm, and a knock at your door revealed a mother with an unconscious child? Or, how would you like to work on an island with no ambulance crew, and where you have to take casualties to meet the air ambulance which lands on one of the island's many sandy beaches?

If these scenarios fill you with dread, then perhaps remote work is not for you. But if, on the other hand, you have an adventurous spirit, then read on.

The UK has some of the most sparsely populated and inhospitable places in Europe. They are also among the most beautiful places in the world. If the 40 minute commute across city gridlock each morning is getting you down, consider trying the drive from Scourie to Kinlochbervie in the Western Highlands instead. Some of the best scenery in Europe lies between these two branch surgeries.

Doctors have to deal with a wide range of medical emergencies with long transport times to hospital. Some areas do not have access to land ambulances, and GPs have to liaise with air ambulance, air-sea rescue helicopters, or lifeboat crews.

More info:

The British Association for Immediate Care[*] (BASICS) is a charity that assists doctors involved in Immediate Care by providing education and support across the UK.

Practices should have an extensive selection of emergency equipment. There is a list of suggestions for the kind of equipment that you may be given when you cover remote areas in Appendix D at the end of this book.

Tip:

You may want to invest in some of this equipment yourself, and everything in the list can be purchased from SP Services.

http://www.999supplies.com

---

[*] http://www.basics.org.uk

Prison Medicine

Locum work in prisons offers an opportunity to try primary care in a quite unusual environment. Having said that, it really can be pretty depressing and stressful, hence the problems that many prisons have in providing a high quality service.

What to look for when arranging prison locum work

Before accepting locum work in prisons, it is sensible to:

- Visit the unit. What are the healthcare staff like? Is the unit well funded and well run? The nurses will be your eyes and ears, so can you trust them, or are they burnt out key janglers?

- How safe is the prison? Minimum security prisons are not much of a problem, but your safety in a high security facility, which will have a significant proportion of violent offenders, will depend on how well run the prison is, and how experienced the guards there are.

- Find out how long they will keep you waiting in reception before transferring you in/out of the health care unit.

Note:

It can take up to an hour to process a member of staff or visitor in some high security facilities, including random searches.

Personal Safety

Personal safety is paramount in prison medicine. You will have prison guards present in the health care unit to protect you, but during consultations you will usually be alone with a prisoner with one or two guards stationed outside. Safety can be compromised by cutbacks in the prison service, serious overcrowding, and the introduction of for-profit private prisons with a high turnover of staff, or a high percentage of inexperienced staff.

Anecdote:

I was working in a private prison healthcare unit. The guards were inexperienced, and in the space of one afternoon two prisoners 'kicked off' during consultations. One threw my desk over and threatened the nurse and me, bringing the experienced prison nurse to tears.

On my way home, I was so stressed out that I was short with a checkout girl in Boots, upsetting her, and I suffered the ire of my fellow shoppers whilst trying to apologise.

I decided to stop working in that prison at that point.

On call prison work

If you are on call then you will be tied to the phone/mobile for emergencies. It matters not a jot that you only get one emergency per month, you will need to be able to drop everything and dash in to the prison. This means you can't really take the kids to the cinema or Pizza Hut (unless you like leaving them in a prison car park for 2 hours).

Risk taking

You need to be willing to take risks in prison health care. 90% of what your patients tell you is probably untrue, so you need to be able to say 'I don't believe this person is sick', which is quite different from normal general practice.

Drug mules and prison healthcare

Healthcare is a favored route for drugs to move around the prison, as it is one of the few locations prisoners can 'arrange' to be.

It is common for prisoners to fake illness, or to be injured deliberately, so as to gain access to the healthcare unit and/or an external hospital (where security is more difficult) with a view to collecting or delivering illegal drugs.

Anecdote:

On one occasion, I saw a patient who was faking unilateral weakness and was sent to the local hospital for a CT scan. Whilst in hospital, he was passed drugs in a condom by a family member who had arranged to be in the lift at the same time as he was being transported. He then stored the drugs in his rectum and was supposed to pass them on to another prisoner on return to the prison healthcare facility.

The dealer on his wing had given one of the other inmates in the wing the choice of having a couple of teeth knocked out or being killed. He had wisely chosen to have his teeth knocked out, and was promptly admitted to our healthcare unit in order to obtain the drugs from the first prisoner.

Sadly for them, by the time the now toothless prisoner arrived, the condom containing the drugs had leaked and the original prisoner had already been sent back out to the hospital in a coma.

> *Caution:*
>
> Make sure the inmates can't find out where you live or who your family are. One way to get drugs in is to threaten staff or their families, and then get them to transport drugs in from the outside (hence the random searches of staff).

Prison work can be an interesting change from general practice, especially if you have a high tolerance for risk. But you need to factor the disadvantages into your rate, or you won't do prison locums for long.

Working in Canada

Introduction to working in Canada

The Canadians are friendly, welcoming people and working there is a great experience (many GPs who go there don't come back to the UK!). However, they are cursed with a terribly bureaucratic immigration system that can easily ruin your best laid plans. So read the following advice carefully.

Each province has its own legislature and its own medical registration boards. This means that procedures and requirements for working as a doctor vary from province to province.

There are three stages to working as a locum in Canada.

- finding work
- getting all the paperwork sorted out
- other things to do before you go

> ### *Caution:*
>
> This section is based on my experiences in 2001. Some or all of the details may have changed since then, so please check the specifics of your application with your potential employer and the relevant agencies.

Eligibility to work

Before you start looking for work you need to find out which provinces you will be eligible to work in.

Rules vary from province to province, and the links to their web sites change with alarming regularity. So I recommend searching on Google with 'college of physicians' and the name of the province you are interested in:

- Alberta
- Nova Scotia
- British Columbia
- Nunavut
- Ontario
- Manitoba
- Prince Edward Island
- Newfoundland
- Quebec
- New Brunswick
- Northwest Territories
- Saskatchewan
- Yukon

Requirements vary by province but on average you will find that they will require:

- Full UK training GP training.
- 8 weeks each of post grad medicine, surgery, paediatrics and obstetrics/gynaecology (PRHO counts).
- 4 weeks each of post grad psychiatry, A&E and general practice.

> **Anecdote:**
>
> I initially had problems with my application to work in Saskatchewan because the administrator was unhappy that some of my training had been done in Scotland. "We don't have Scotland on our list of recognised countries for training purposes. We've got Britain and Ireland, but not Scotland". She initially didn't believe me when I pointed out that Scotland was part of Britain.

> **Note:**
>
> Canadians call hospital medicine 'Internal Medicine'. They don't use the term 'General Medicine', and may confuse this with 'General Practice' (which they also call 'Family Practice'). So you should amend your CV to reflect this.

Some provinces require you to sit the Evaluating Exam for International Medical Graduates before you are allowed to practice at all. The Evaluating Exam is run by the Medical Council of Canada (MCC)[*] and costs around C$900 (approximately £400) and is held twice a year in London. However, most provinces will allow you to work for up to a year before you have to take this exam[†].

---

[*] Website http://www.mcc.ca

[†] But beware – should you fail the Evaluating Exam while you are working in Canada the Colleges are liable to revoke your temporary licence until you take the exam again and pass.

> *Note:*
>
> If you are planning on emigrating permanently, then things get more complicated. You will need to sit the Evaluating Exam for International Medical Graduates and will usually be given a time limit to pass the Certification Exam of the College of Family Physicians of Canada (CCFP). You may need to agree to remain in an under-doctored area for several years or until you pass your CCFP.

Finding Canadian locum work

You can't apply for a work permit for Canada until you have a firm offer of work - so you need to find work before you can continue with any paperwork.

Try looking in the BMJ classifieds or visit the websites of the provincial physician recruiters: again, I recommend searching on Google with 'physician recruitment' and the name of the province you are interested in.

They are pretty desperate for locums in the remote and rural areas, but you are much less likely to find work in the cities.

Canadian Income

Canadian family physicians are paid mainly fee-for-service, and this is where most of your earnings will come from.

Physicians in a group deduct a percentage of their fee for service work to cover overheads (secretarial staff, accounting fees etc.), so you will usually be offered between a 50:50 split and a 85:15 split by your employer. A 70:30 split or better is desirable.

Caution:

Anything below a 60:40 split in income is suspect (i.e. your employer keeps more than 40% of what you earn towards the cost of running the practice).

He/she may be keeping some of your earnings as profit for him/herself, not as overhead payments, or the practice may be mismanaged.

GPs also get paid for on call work, hospital duties, emergency room work etc.. You should expect to keep 100% of these fees unless there is a good reason otherwise.

Earnings for full time family practice in Canada in 2001 were around C$13,000 to C$20,000 dollars per month before tax.

Canadian Tax

You will need to contact an accountant when you are in Canada to discuss how much tax you will need to pay, and how to go about paying it.

Tax rates are slightly higher than in the UK, and you should plan to put aside around 30-35% of your income for tax, but this varies with the amount you earn and which province you are in.

In general, the Canadian tax system is less generous with allowable expenses than HM Revenue and Customs.

> *Important:*
>
> Canada and the UK have a tax agreement. So, whatever tax you pay in Canada will be credited to your account in the UK.
>
> This means that although you have to declare your Canadian income in the UK (assuming you work in both countries during the same tax year), you will only pay tax once on this income. Talk to your UK accountant about this.

Canadian expenses

You need to think about how much getting to and being in Canada is going to cost you.

That includes:

- flights
- car rental
- accommodation costs
- indemnity
- registration fees
- immigration fees
- mail forwarding
- mobile communications
- storage of property/vehicles while you are away

Who will pay for my expenses?

This varies from province to province and locum to locum.

There is federal money for rural areas to pay the expenses of attracting locums to work there.

Some provinces use this expense budget to pay for your flights, accommodation, vehicle hire and even your indemnity up to a set maximum per month/year

> *Example:*
>
> Prince Edward Island will pay up to $2500 dollars per month, up to a maximum of $7500 in any one year, for these expenses.
>
> Saskatchewan, on the other hand, has no federal funds available for individual locums.

However, other provinces have spent this money to set up salaried locum schemes to provide temporary relief cover for small rural practices. This means there is no federal money for your expenses, you will need to come to an agreement with the practice as to how the costs will be split.

You should be aiming for the practice/physician to pay for:

- Your flight costs to and from the locum.

- Your accommodation costs.

- Your vehicle hire on the weeks you are actually working.

But remember that if the practice/physician employing you does not pay for these costs then that should be reflected in your earnings. So if it is a good split of earnings then you may be willing to accept poorer expense reimbursement. If you are unhappy with the overall package, shop around. Much will depend on how much work is available at the time.

Ok - you've found a practice looking for a locum, your pretty certain you can get temporary registration in than province, you have worked out roughly how much it will cost you, who is paying for what and how much you are going to earn.

The easy bit is over - now it's time for...

The Paperwork

Human Resources Canada

Even once you do find an offer of work, it needs to be assessed by Human Resources Canada (another unanswerable government agency) to see if the post could be filled by a Canadian.

Only once they are satisfied that the employer has made adequate attempts to find a suitable Canadian for the job (and failed) will they authorise the job for Immigration purposes. The practice or physician employing you will sort this out, which will take about one to two weeks on average.

While you are waiting for this authorisation, you can begin to put together the rest of your paperwork...

Provincial College of Physicians Paperwork

Before you can apply for a work permit you will need confirmation from the provincial College of Physicians that you are eligible to practice in that province.

This is pretty easy, as all you need to do is send some paperwork to the appropriate College of Physicians - they are usually extremely helpful.

The easiest way initially is to fax or email them your CV with a covering note - but when you arrive you will need to go for an interview with them before you can start work. Sometimes the practice will handle the initial part with the local College for you.

Eventually, for your interview, you will need to produce the following paperwork - you'll need a lot of this pretty soon for Immigration Canada (see below) anyway, so you might as well start getting it together now:

1. Registration Fee - around $150-$200 per month, payable in advance in Canadian funds only (it's best to take cash)

2. Evidence of your qualifications - original degree and diploma / higher qualification certificates

3. Curriculum Vitae -qualifications and diplomas, ALL the substantive posts you have held, 3 referees of good character (and their FAX numbers)

4. A copy of a letter from each training post administrator with the duration of your training in that post, the specialities you covered, and a statement that your performance in post was satisfactory

5. documentation from the General Medical Council - certificate of registration and a Certificate of Good Standing dated within the past three months

6. a photograph of approximately passport size

7. proof of your identity (passport - the name on your passport should match the name on your other documents).

Immigration Canada Paperwork

This is where the fun starts (you might as well order that first box of Prozac now).

You need a work permit from Immigration Canada[*] before you can work in Canada. **You must apply for and receive this before you travel to Canada.**

---

[*] Website http://www.canada.org.uk

To make an application for a work permit you need the following:

- Application form[*]

- Processing fee : Canadian money only, around $150, which needs to be a bank draft made out to the "Receiver General for Canada". Don't send cash, they won't accept it, but they will accept pounds sterling in cash if you attend in person (see below).

- Photocopy of Passport ID page - if you are a British/EU Citizen you only need to send a photocopy of the ID page from their passport. (Other nationals may need to send their actual passport - see paperwork with application form)

- Photographs - 2 passport sized photographs

- Letter from your prospective employer offering employment - must contain: exact job title (e.g.: Locum Family Medical Practitioner), the actual duties involved (eg: clinic responsibilities, on call duties, emergency room duties, hospital duties etc.), the actual salary structure and expected salary, the start date for employment, the duration of employment, the Human Resources Canada authorisation number[†].

- Evidence of your qualifications - curriculum vitae and copies of your qualifications and diplomas

- Proof of funds (i.e.: a copy of a recent bank statement showing a nice healthy balance)

- Medical Report - this has to be carried out at a registered centre (there are five in Scotland) and there is a four to eight

---

[*] Form number IMM5256, available from the Canadian High Commission in London. You can't phone them, you need to visit in person or write to them: Canadian High Commission, MacDonald House, 38 Grosvenor Street, London W1X 0AA.

[†] you can make an application before this arrives, but your application won't be processed until you fax/post this to them, and if you do not receive authorisation you won't get your $150 back.

week waiting list for appointments (so if it's urgent, tell the staff and try and get squeezed in earlier). It includes a VDRL blood test and a Chest X-ray, it costs about £150 and once you've had your medical expect another 2 -3 week wait (at least) until your work permit is issued. They will send you details of how to organise your medical report 2 to 4 weeks after you submit your application.

Tip:

If you are applying in person remember to ask for the list of accredited doctors there and then so you can organise your medical in advance.

The paperwork part feels nothing short of impossible. This is due almost entirely to the bureaucracy of Immigration Canada. Having said that, it appears that doctors are actually receiving pretty special treatment – lesser mortals can expect the process to last up to 18 months.

If you fail to give Immigration Canada any of the above paperwork, and need to send it later, you can add another 2 to 4 weeks on to the process per batch of paperwork.

This page will help guide you through this remarkable process, but no amount of help will be enough - for no matter what paperwork you present, or how organised you think you have been, they seem to always find something else that they need you to fill in.

Note that it is very difficult to contact Immigration Canada except by post and by fax (the telephone number gives out recorded information only). They take up to four weeks to reply to any mail or faxes (if they reply at all), and if you do contact them, they say that your application will be delayed (because they take your application out of the pile to answer your query, and then return it to the back of the queue!) Having said that, I have heard tales of occasional, kindly immigration officials hiding in the department who have helped 'bump' an application closer to the top of the pile when the urgency was explained to them.

Also note that Immigration Canada have a habit of sending you unannounced, vital fax information about what you should do next. Should you fail to get the fax and they have not heard from you within 30 days, then they close your file and you have to start all over again.

So basically you won't know when your work permit will arrive, if at all, and there is no way that anyone can find out (unless you want to wait four weeks for the answer) unless you go to the High Commission in London in person.

Tip:

If you do go to the High Commission in person you should turn up before 11 am (as anyone arriving after 11 am is not allowed in).

Be prepared to wait in a long queue, often starting well outside the building, for up to 3 or 4 hours.

This all makes for a deeply frustrating process, because until the work permit arrives you cannot travel to Canada.

The whole thing appears to take about 3 months on average from start to finish and is a lot of work.

What should I arrange before I travel?

You will need to sort out the following before you travel:

Flights to Canada

- Don't book non-changeable or non-refundable tickets until you have your work permit in hand and exact dates of travel.

- If you are going for more than 1-3 months then the tickets tend to be much more expensive.

- It may be cheaper to buy bargain return tickets and throw away the return portion of the ticket, then do the same when you want to come home.

Canadian Indemnity

Canadian medical indemnity is provided though the Canadian Medical Protection Association[*] (CMPA), and is surprisingly cheap. Depending on the strength of the pound against the Canadian dollar, you can expect your indemnity to cost almost half of what it costs in the UK.

Remember to suspend your UK indemnity for the time you are away – defence organisations will usually continue Samaritan cover for the period that you are away, even in North America.

Sending and receiving post in Canada

You can arrange a postal address in Canada through Mail Boxes Etc.[†], and the UK Mail Boxes Etc.[‡] can arrange periodic mail forwarding from the UK (although it can be expensive).

---

[*] http://www.cmpa-acpm.ca/

[†] http://www.mbe.ca/

[‡] http://www.mbe.uk.com/

> *Note:*
>
> Canada Post (their version of the Royal Mail) is terrible. It can take six days for a letter to reach an address just down the street from you. So for anything remotely important or urgent, most Canadians use a courier service such as Fed-Ex or UPS.

Mobile Phones in Canada

Before you go, arrange with your service provider for your mobile phone to take international calls – sometimes you can pay a monthly fee for cheaper international calls.

Remember that you will need a tri-band phone if you want to use it in North America, and that mobile coverage is not nearly as good in the US and Canada as it is in Europe.

You can rent a mobile phone when you get there (from the car rental company) but call costs are higher than here. Also, you can buy a 'pay as you go' phone in Canada relatively cheaply, which is cost effective for longer trips.

Sending and receiving email in Canada

Open an email account with AOL[*] or Compuserve[†] as they have free access numbers in the US (remember, local calls in North America are free).

You can still pick up email from your own email account using the local dial-up number, or you can forward your email to the new account or you can use an online email account such as Doctors.net.uk[‡].

---

[*] http://www.aol.com/

[†] http://webcenters.netscape.compuserve.com

[‡] http://www.doctors.net.uk

Vehicles

You can drive in most provinces in Canada for three months on your UK drivers licence – if you plan to be there for more than three months, you will need to sit a Canadian driving text.

You may need to garage your car while you are away, and you can save money on the vehicle tax by making a SORN declaration to the DVLA[*]. You can also save money on insurance by making it just fire and theft insurance.

On the other hand, if you let your friends / family look after the vehicle while you are away, make sure that their (or your) insurance covers them to drive the vehicle.

Housing

If you rent accommodation, your landlord may not be happy at the property being left empty for more than 2 weeks - discuss this with them prior to travelling. You need to discuss your absence with your household insurance company as well.

Consider switching off you BT account and TV licence to save money while you are away. For longer trips, you may even want to give up rented accommodation, or let out your house, while you are away.

Summary

Although the process of getting to Canada to work is every bit as difficult as this section makes out, I worked in Saskatchewan for four months in 2001, and we have very fond memories of our time there. Canada is a wonderful country to live in. I've yet to meet a Canadian that I disliked, and GP morale is better than it is in the UK.

---

[*] http://www.vehiclelicence.gov.uk

Appendices

A. Useful locum websites

Locum websites

These are some of the main locum websites in the UK:

locum123.com - http://www.locum123.com

National Association of Sessional GPs http://www.nasgp.org.uk

Locum discussion forums

Where locums meet to discuss topics of interest:

Doctors.net – NP discussion forum http://www.doctors.net.uk

Clinical information websites

British National Formulary - http://www.bnf.org.uk

eMedicine – online medical textbook - http://www.emedicine.com

GANFYD medical encyclopedia - http://ganfyd.org

Websites of locum GPs

There are quite a few locum GPs around the country that have set up their own locum websites that are a useful resource:

http://www.drjohnson.co.uk

http://www.hillsidehouse.co.uk

http://www.geocities.com/rmlmtl

http://www.coull.net

http://www.geocities.com/drajcole

http://www.gplocumservice.co.uk

http://www.londonlocum.co.uk

http://www.dace.co.uk

http://www.djm.gb.net

http://www.locumnw.co.uk

http://www.doctormiller.co.uk

http://www.twinn.cc

http://www.locumgps.com

http://www.jondarlington.f2s.com

http://www.ianward.org

http://www.drwheeler.co.uk

Web-building sites

If you are interested in building your own locum website, then these links can be useful:

http://www.geocities.com/rmlmtl

http://www.siterightnow.com

Other useful websites

Apple computers - http://www.apple.com

British Association for Immediate Care - http://www.basics.org.uk

British Medical Association - http://www.bma.org

eFax.com - http://www.efax.com

First Direct Bank - http://www.firstdirect.com

General Medical Council - http://www.gmc-uk.org

HM Revenues and Customs - http://www.hmrc.gov.uk

Information Commissioner -

http://www.informationcommissioner.gov.uk

Mail Boxes Etc. - http://www.mbe.uk.com

Medical Council of Canada - http://www.mcc.ca

Movietrak – online DVD rental by post –

http://www.movietrak.co.uk/

Paypal - www.paypal.com

Pensions Agency - http://www.nhspa.gov.uk

Postgraduate Medical Education & Training Board –

http://www.pmetb.org.uk

Rubberstampz - http://www.rubberstampz.co.uk

Spinvox voicemail - http://www.spinvox.com

SP Services – medical supplies - http://www.999supplies.com/

Appendix B: Useful addresses

British Medical Association

Tel +44 (0)20 7387 4499

BMA House
Tavistock Square
London
WC1H 9JP

Information Commissioner

Tel +44 (0)1625 545740

Notification Department
The Office of the Information Commissioner
Wycliffe House
Water Lane
Wilmslow

General Medical Council

Tel +44 (0)20 7580 7642

178 Great Portland Street
London
W1N 6AE

Joint Committee on Postgraduate Training for General Practice

Tel +44 (0)207 581 3232

14 Princes Gate
London
SW7 1PU

NHS Pension Agency England and Wales

Tel +44 (0)1253 774774

Hesketh House
200-220 Broadway,
Fleetwood
Lancashire
FY7 8LG

Scottish Office Pension Agency

Tel +44 (0)131 244 3585

St Margaret's House
151, London Road
Edinburgh
EH8 7TG

Appendix C: Useful Locum Forms

You may find the following template documents useful. You can download full size copies of these templates from the locum123.com website:

http://www.locum123.com/survival_pack.shtml

You are free to modify, copy, and use these templates, so long as you leave the link to locum123.com and the © notice in the footer at the bottom of any copies that you make,

Practice Details Sheet

Practice Details Sheet

PRACTICE DETAILS SHEET

Main Details

Name of Practice	
Street	
City	
Area	
Postcode	

	Telephone	Fax	Email	Website
Practice Manager				
GPs				
Practice Nurse				

Other numbers	Telephone
Dispensary	
Treatment room	
Health Visitor	
District Nurses	
Social Services	
Police	
Ambulance	
CPN	
Undertaker	

Reception Staff

Hospitals/Pharmacies	Telephone	Fax	Address	Notes

You are free to modify, copy, and use this fax cover sheet so long as you leave the link to locum123.com and the © notice in the footer at the bottom of the page.

Locum Doctor's Survival Guide **www.locum123.com** ©R Croft 1999-2006 and locum123.com ltd 2002-2003

Practice Clinics Sheet

Practice Clinics Sheet

PRACTICE DETAILS   SHEET   Name of Practice

(c)locum123.com, 2004

Clinics	Referral Method	Telephone	Address	Notes
Alcohol Detox				
Antenatal Clinic				
Asthma Clinic				
Breast Clinic and Mammography				
Chiropody				
Diabetic Clinic				
Dietitian				
Drug Addiction Services				
Family Planning and IUCDs				
Joint Injections				
Minor ops				
Physiotherapy				
Smears				
STD Clinic				
Travel Advice				
Terminations				
Warts				

Referral Methods: letter, telephone, dedicated form, in-practice

You are free to modify, copy, and use this fax cover sheet so long as you leave the link to locum123.com and the © notice in the footer at the bottom of the page.

Locum Doctor's Survival Guide   www.locum123.com   ©R Gault 1999-2008 and locum123.com ltd 2001-2005

Emergency Referral Form

Your Letterhead Goes Here

You are free to modify, copy, and use this sheet so long as you leave the link to locum123.com and the © notice in the footer at the bottom of the page.

EMERGENCY REFERRAL

A full referral letter will/will not* be faxed to the hospital

Date:

Patient's Details:

Patient's Own GP:

Hospital Ward:

Hx:

OE:

Rx:

Please take this letter with you and give it to the doctor at the hospital

*delete as appropriate

Dictation List

Your Letterhead Goes Here

You are free to modify, copy, and use this dictation sheet so long as you leave the link to locum123.com and the © notice in the footer at the bottom of the page.

Use one form per dictation tape. Place tape in a sealed envelope and staple envelope to form.

Dictated	Patient Details	Referrred to	Signed

Note to secretary: Please place date in the 'signed' column when letter has been checked, signed and sent. Once all letters have been completed and signed, please return this form or post it to the address on the letterhead. Thank you.

www.locum123.com

Locum Doctor's Survival Guide   R Coull 1999-2005 and locum123.com ltd 2001-2005

Quotation and Confirmation Form

Your Letterhead Goes Here

You are free to modify, copy, and use this sheet so long as you leave the link to locum123.com and the © notice in the footer at the bottom of the page.

Practice Address Goes Here

Dear Practice Manager,

Re: Locum cover

I am pleased to be able to offer GP locum cover for your unit.

Please check the dates, fees and terms and conditions to make sure that they are satisfactory. If you have any questions or comments, don't hesitate to contact me to discuss your requirements.

If you are happy with the quote, please sign and date the bottom of the form and fax the **entire document** back to me on **INSERT FAX NUMBER** to confirm your booking.

Dates:

Start Date	Start Time	Finish Date	Finish Time

Fees:

Item	Rate	Number	Sub-total
Daytime cover (8.30-5.30)			
OOH rate (5.30 – 11.30)			
OOH rate (11.30 – 8.30)			
Accommodation and subsistence			
Travel mileage	XXp/mile return		
Ferry/Airfare			
Total			

Terms and Conditions:

Your Terms and Conditions Go Here

www.locum123.com   ©R Coull 1999-2005 and locum123.com ltd 2001-2005

Yours sincerely,

DR YOUR NAME
Locum GP

....

I would like to book locum cover for the above dates. I have read, and agree to, the above
terms and conditions.

Signed: .... Date: ....

Name: .... Designation: ....

Fax Confidentiality Cover Sheet

Your Letterhead Goes Here

You are free to modify, copy, and use this fax cover sheet so long as you leave the link to locum123.com and the © notice in the footer at the bottom of the page.

FAX MESSAGE

From:	
To:	
Fax Number:	
Date:	Friday, November 18, 2005
Number of pages (including this one):	

Memo:

CONFIDENTIALITY NOTICE

This facsimile transmission is intended only for the use of the individual or entity to which it is addressed and may contain confidential information belonging to the sender which is protected by the physician-patient privilege and should only be read by those persons to whom it is addressed. If you are not the intended recipient, you are hereby notified that any copying, disclosure, distribution, or the taking of any action in reliance of the contents of this information is strictly prohibited. If you have received this transmission in error, please call the number on the letterhead to arrange return of the documents at our expense.

www.locum123.com

NHS Pension Scheme – GP Locum Form A

GP LOCUM A

GP Locum use only

NHS Pension Scheme - GP Locum's monthly certificate of NHS work and pay for one GP Practice

To claim NHS Scheme membership for GP Locum NHS work, you must complete PART 1 of this form and send it with your monthly invoice to the appropriate GP Practice. You will need a separate form for any additional GP Practices.

Only NHS GP Locum services contracted directly between a GP Locum and a NHS GP Practice for an absent GP(s) may be entered on this form. GP Locum work contracted with organisations outside the NHS, eg. Cooperatives, multifunds, etc., cannot be pensionable in the NHS Scheme.

Part1. To be completed by the GP Locum

Your name

National Insurance number

Host HA / PCT

Host HA / PCT Registration No.

Please enter below the dates you worked for the GP Practice.

From   /   /   to   /   /   From   /   /   to   /   /

From   /   /   to   /   /   From   /   /   to   /   /

Signature

Date   /   /

I claim NHS Scheme membership for the NHS work I undertook for the practice named in Part 2 below.

Part 2 To be completed by the GP Practice Authorised Signatory (eg. practice manager, partner)

GP Locum's gross pay for the NHS work shown in Part 1 above.   £

Which absent GP(s) was this work done for, or which GP(s) have you provided cover for?

Name

GP Practice code

GP Practice stamp

Declaration
I certify that this practice has paid the GP Locum the gross amount shown for the NHS work declared in Part 1.

Signature

Date of payment   /   /

3/2003

NHS Pension Scheme – GP Locum Form B

GP LOCUM B
NHS Pension Scheme - **GP Locum's monthly record of all NHS locum pay and related pension contributions**

GPLocum use only

Surname	Other names		Sex (M/F)	Date of birth
NI number	NHSPS ref number	Host HA / PCT	Host HA / PCT reference no.	
Address			Calendar Month	
	Postcode		Year 20......	

PART 1

GP Practice code	Name of GP Practice	First day worked for this payment	Last day worked for this payment	Date gross pay received	Gross Pay £	p

PART 2

For HA / PCT use only

Total Contributions

Employee	£
Employer	£

Total of gross NHS locum pay	a
Professional expenses deduction (a x 10%)	b
Net NHS pensionable pay (a – b)	c
NHS Scheme gross employee contributions (c x 6%)	d
Total of any NHS extra % added years contributions (c x %)	e
Total of any NHS extra % AVCs (c x % or agreed sum)	f
Grand total of NHS Pension Scheme gross employee contributions (d or d + e/f)	g

IMPORTANT Now attach a cheque to this form, payable to your Host HA / PCT, for the total amount at (g) above and send it to arrive no later than the 7th day of the month, following the month this form relates to. You must attach a properly completed form GP Locum A for every payment declared on this form.

3/2001

Appendix D: Locum Equipment

General consulting

- A4 paper, GP111 pink sheets, envelopes, blood forms and x-ray forms
- Needles and syringes
- Gauze swabs, plasters and alcohol wipes
- Disposable ear probes for thermometer and auroscope
- Pregnancy urine test kits(eg: Clear Blue™)
- Toys
- Gestational calculator
- British National Formulary (BNF), Medical Dictionary and portable textbooks (eg: Oxford Handbook of General Practice)
- Rubber stamps
- Latex gloves
- Urine dipsticks
- Peakflow tubes and demonstration spacer with inhaler
- sphygmomanometer
- stethoscope
- Mini ophthalmoscope
- Mini auroscope
- Maglite AA torch
- Digital thermometer
- peak flow meter

- mini oxygen saturation monitor
- glucometer
- ultra violet light
- swabs
- tourniquet
- sharps box
- pocket mask
- lubricating jelly
- blood tubes
- butterfly needles
- eye drops
- urine sample bottles

General Items

- A good set of road maps
- Polaroid™ camera and film / Digital camera
- Sturdy all-weather torches(eg: Maglite™)
- Warning triangles x2
- Vomit bowls
- Alcohol hand gel (water free for use in the car)
- Clinical waste bags
- Paper roll

Out of Hours Drugs

- amoxycillin 250mg tabs
- erythromycin 250mg tabs

- chlorpheniramine 4mg tabs
- ibuprofen 200mg tabs
- metoclopramide 10mg tabs
- paracetamol 500mg tabs
- paracetamol 120mg soluble tabs
- prednisolone 5mg tabs
- trimethoprim 200mg tabs

BASICS Emergency Equipment

Personal Protective Equipment
- BASICS squad suit
- high visibility jacket
- high visibility tabard
- full face protective helmet
- heavy duty gloves
- folding road cones x6
- High powered rechargeable torch

Major items
- Oxygen cylinder and regulator
- Defibrillator
- 12 lead ECG machine
- carry chair/folding stretcher
- box splints

Adult Emergency Bag

- Sutures, steristrips and gauze swabs

- dressings and bandages

- 500 mls iv fluid and giving set

- disposable suture pack, dressing packs, saline sachets, scalpels

- adult bag-valve-mask

- sphygmomanometer

- adult ET tubes

- surgical cricothyroidotomy kit (eg: minitrach II™)

- needle cricothyroidotomy kit

- suction unit (eg: vvac™)

- space blankets

- hard cervical collars (eg: Stiffneck™)

Adult Tool roll

- scissors (eg: Tuff Cut™)

- nasopharyngeal airways

- adult guedel airways

- adult magill forceps

- adult laryngoscopes x2

- tourniquet

- adult iv splint (eg: Armlock™)

- iv cannulae (eg: Venflons™)

- syringes and iv flush

- catheter mount connector

- tape

Paediatric Emergency Bag

- 250 mls iv fluid and three way tap giving set
- intraosseous needles x2
- child and infant bag-valve-mask
- small sphygmomanometer cuff
- paediatric ET tubes
- surgical cricothyroidotomy kit
- cord clamps
- maternity pack
- paediatric hard cervical collars

Paediatric tool roll

- nasopharyngeal airways
- child guedel airways
- child magill forceps
- paediatric laryngoscopes x3
- child iv splint
- paediatric iv cannulae

Emergency Drugs

- activated charcoal 5 grams
- adenosine 6mg x4
- adrenaline 1:1,000 vials x6
- adrenaline 1:1,000 minijet
- adrenaline 1:10,000 minijet x2
- aminophylline 250mg/10mls

- aspirin 300mg
- atropine 1mg minijet x3
- benzyl penicillin 600mg x4
- budesonide 1mg nebs
- cefotaxime 500mg
- cefotaxime 1 gram
- chlorpheniramine 10mg iv
- diamorphine 10mg x5 (held separately)
- diazepam 5mg pr x2
- diazepam 10mg iv x2
- diclofenac 75mg im x2
- diclofenac 100mg pr x2
- digoxin 500mcg iv
- droperidol 5mg im
- flumazenil 500mcg x2
- frusemide 50mg iv x2
- glucagon
- glucose 50% 50mls
- glucose gel (oral)
- GTN spray
- GTN iv 5mg/5mls x2
- hydrocortisone 100mg iv x2
- ipratropium bromide 250mcg nebs
- lignocaine 100mg minijet
- lignocaine 1% x10mls
- magnesium sulphate 20mmol/10mls
- metoclopramide 10mg iv

- midazolam 10mg/2ml
- naloxone 400mcg x3
- salbutamol 5mg nebs
- saline for injection
- suscard buccal 5mg tabs
- syntometrine 5iu/500mcg
- water for injection

Personal Items

- Cordless telephone / answering machine - to take into the bathroom, garden etc. You can put your mobile number on the answering machine to avoid missing calls if you are out. Get a DECT mobile phone to ensure your calls cannot be overheard.

- DVD films - most laptop computers play DVDs which you can order online to be delivered anywhere in the UK by post (one week rental is £3.50 per DVD at movietrak.com)

- Wireless internet connection (WiFi) - allows you to go online without having to be near a phone socket. You will need a base station and a wireless card for your laptop. Available from most computer shops.

- Small portable speakers - to plug into your laptop for DVDs or playing music CDs.

- Extension cables - there will never be enough power sockets in your room so take along a couple of multi-socket adapters.

- Smoke / CO detector - peace of mind for those who suffer from catastrophic thinking.

- Travel kettle and tea bags / coffee - to use in your room.

- Fan heater - a small fan heater unit will help you heat cold locum residences in the winter and cool them down in the summer.

- Portable printer - you can buy small portable printers very cheaply, then you have a mobile office and can take care of most of your business paperwork on the move.

Appendix E: Suggested Reading

Running your own business

Sara Williams (2001) <u>Lloyds TSB Small Business Guide.</u> 15th ed. London, Press Vitesse.

Vera Hughes and David Weller (1997) <u>Teach Yourself Setting Up a Small Business.</u> London, Hodder and Stoughton.

Patricia Clayton (2002) <u>The Sunday Times Business Enterprise Guide: Forming a Limited Company.</u> 7th ed. London, Kogan Page.

Peter Taylor (2003) <u>Book Keeping and Accounting for the Small Business.</u> 7th Ed. Oxford, How To Books.

John Whiteley (2003) <u>Small Business Tax Guide.</u> Oxford, How To Books.

Alvin Hall (2002) <u>Your Money or Your Life.</u> London, Hodder and Stoughton.

Negotiation

Roger Fisher and William Ury (1999) <u>Getting to Yes.</u> 2nd ed. London, Random House

Phil Baguley (2003) <u>Teach Yourself Negotiating.</u> London, Hodder and Stoughton.

Michael and Mimi Donaldson (1996) <u>Negotiation for Dummies.</u> New York, Wiley.

Tim Handle (1998) <u>Negotiating Skills.</u> London, Dorling Kindersley.

Variety in locum work

Janet Macdonald (2001) <u>Living and Working in Canada</u>. London, Survival Books.

Miscellaneous

Richard Koch (1998) <u>The 80/20 Principle</u>. London, Nicholas Brealey Publishing.

Elizabeth Castro (2003) <u>HTML for the World Wide Web</u>. 5th ed. Berkley, Peachpit Press.

Index

penalties for late payment.. 55
problems obtaining payment 64
terms 55
payment options...... See payment
Paypal™ 62
PCO Complaints See Complaints
PCOsSee Primary Care Organisations
pdf files 59
peak flow meter 185
peak times 37
Penalites for late paymentSee payment
pension contributions 84
pensions 91
    NHS Pension Agency England and Wales 172
    NHS pension scheme...91, 93
    private pensions 94
    Scottish Office Pension Agency 172
performers............................. 107
performers list................. 92, 109
    English performers list..... 109
    Scottish Performers List .. 109
    Welsh Performers List 109
personal borrowing.. See banking
Personal items........................ 118
personal loan............ See banking
personal Protective equipment 187
personnel departments........... 8, 9
pets 122
plan ahead 5
pocket mask 186
Polaroid camera 186
poor care 135
poorly performing doctor 135
portable printer 192
portable speakers 191
post.. 119
    mail forwarding.................. 56

post-graduate education............. 9
Postgraduate Medical Education and Training Board108, 110, 111
practicalities of locum work.. 107
practice clinics sheet............. 175
practice details sheet............. 175
practice manager............... 10, 23
Practice meetings.................. 129
prednisolone........................... 187
pregnancy urine test kits........ 185
prescribing numbers 112
prescribing patterns 112
Primary Care Organisations 40
Primary-Secondary Care CommunicationSee Communication
prison medicine..................... 147
privacy..................................... ii
private pensions ...... See pensions
private prescription............... 114
private work 44
problems obtaining paymentSee payment
professional development...... 112
professional misconductSee General Medical Council
profits
    maximise profits................. 32
provisional bookings 104
Public Companies limited by guaranteeSee Limited Companies
public liability insurance 24
public transport ...... See expenses
public transport costsSee expenses
putting money aside for taxSee tax

Q
qualifications......................... 107
Quicken 75

Notes